Ladykiller

Also by Lillian O'Donnell

Ladykiller

Lillian O'Donnell

G. P. PUTNAM'S SONS
New York

Library of Congress Cataloging in Publication Data

O'Donnell, Lillian.
  Ladykiller.

  I. Title.
PS3565.D59L3   1984   813'.54   84-17751
ISBN 0-399-13006-3

PRINTED IN THE UNITED STATES OF AMERICA

Ladykiller

Chapter _____ ONE

April Fool's Day and even the temperature joined in the joke: the daytime high had been ninety-three; at midnight the temperature stuck at eighty-six.

He lay on the convertible sofabed in the front room stripped to boxer shorts, sheet thrown back, thin body oiled in sweat. The window fan brought no relief; it only sucked in a medley of ethnic cooking odors. Though the shades were drawn, the blue neon sign of the bar and grill downstairs kept the room half lit. From the adjoining bedroom Frank could hear his stepfather grunting and his mother moaning. He gritted his teeth and trembled.

The sporadic passing of trains on the elevated section of the Queens-Flushing line rattled the windows and the kitchen china. Spread-eagled on the worn mattress, broken springs jabbing his lanky frame every time he shifted, Frank Salgo stared at the patterns on the ceiling, wide, wide awake. It wasn't much better than the bunk at Spofford. Worse, then he'd had something to look forward to—getting out. Now he was out and more restricted than ever. Security at the correctional facility, supposedly the strictest of the juvenile institutions, had been a laugh; kids came and went, climbing in and out of windows, sometimes even walking out the front door. They brought back booze and junk for the more timid, who paid for it with money or sex. There was school, but what they learned was not what the citizens paid taxes for. The primary lesson was: don't get caught the next time. For some, Frank Salgo among them, the next time would mean trial as an adult. Frank Salgo had passed his sixteenth birthday.

He looked older. In his narrow pale face the dark eyes glittered disproportionately large. Beneath his aquiline nose, pinched just at the nostrils, his lips were sensually full. He had a high forehead, curly black hair swept back from a widow's peak. He was handsome, but already the look of cunning had crept in to spoil it. Still, the girls liked him. Frank knew they did. So far, he wasn't interested.

Frank turned on his side and cursed the noise and the heat and the thin mattress and the lack of privacy. He was fed up. His stepfather, Homer Petrus, was on his case the whole time. Petrus, part owner of the bar and grill over which they lived, had put Frank to work there as a bus boy. By dumping a tray of dirty dishes into a customer's lap, Frank had made sure to get himself fired. Petrus knew it had been on purpose, but what could he do about it? Nag. And he kept at it. *Go to work! Get a job.* Petrus rousted him out of bed in the morning and waited till he came in at night. Frank had to account for every damn hour and every damn dollar. No more. *No more.* Tonight, he was making his move.

In the next room, his mother's thin wail signaled the end of intercourse. A fresh outbreak of sweat cooled Frank's taut frame. He shivered, then lay still. He waited. He waited half an hour by his digital wristwatch to make sure his mother and her husband were sleeping soundly. Then quietly he got up. Chinos, shirt, and jacket were laid out on a chair ready to put on; Adidas sneakers and socks on the floor under it. Alongside was a nylon duffel bag already packed with extra shorts, Walkman, and the knife. By the light of the neon sign, Frank was able to dress quickly. In spite of the heat, he put his jacket on and then took the knife out of the bag, pausing for a moment to enjoy the feel of it in his hand. Best quality steel, the ad had claimed, with a handle perfectly balanced, the blade thin and finely honed—a hunting knife guaranteed to slit the toughest hide, skin the most tender flesh. When he thought of his first weapon, a blunted pen knife, Frank Salgo was ashamed. He'd had to stab the nun over and over and finally leave her without being sure she was really dead. For four days after, Salgo had stayed home cowering every time the doorbell rang.

After a while he'd relaxed. He realized the police didn't know where to look. Now he knew they were spread too thin to waste time on street crime and small heists—neighborhood crime. He became as contemptuous of the police on the outside as he had learned to be of the guards on the inside. The odds were in his favor, heavily in his favor, that he'd never get caught and, even if he did, that he wouldn't serve time. Frank slipped the new, never-used knife up his sleeve and, feeling the haft rest reassuringly against the base of his left hand, he crept over to the bedroom door and listened. Petrus was snoring; his mother . . . he couldn't hear anything from her. She must be asleep by now. Frank turned the knob slowly, as silently as he could. He pushed the door open and, holding his breath, went in.

The room was at the rear of the apartment overlooking other rancid backyards, its only illumination the lights of Manhattan, first reflecting off the waters of the East River then bouncing off the low cloud layer. It took a few moments to get used to the new depths of darkness till he could make out the forms on the bed. The big heavily muscled man lay with his mouth open like a fish, left arm outflung, hairy hand still grasping his mother's bare breast. His mother, coarse black hair spread over the sweat-soaked pillow, satin nightgown plastered to her body and rumpled high over her white thighs, looked spent. The boy stared at the two of them a long time before he turned his back and went to the bureau. He knew exactly where to look. He also knew that after closing Homer Petrus usually walked over to the bank and put the receipts into the night repository. Tonight, it had been stuck, and Petrus had had to bring the take home. Frank gloated. It was what had finally decided him.

He slid open the top bureau drawer. On the right-hand side he found his stepfather's wallet, as usual. Greedily, Frank reached behind it for the canvas money pouch. It wasn't there. He felt through the rest of the contents, fumbling over rolled-up socks, handkerchiefs, extra keys, deodorant sticks, broken rosary beads—Petrus never went to church but he carried his beads. Nothing. He went back to the wallet. It was thin. He opened it and fingered the few bills. What had Petrus done with the receipts? Where had he stashed them? There had to be five or six hundred bucks, Frank figured, maybe more. Carefully, near panic, Frank slid the drawer shut and opened the one below. Shirts, shorts—no money. *Shit!* He probably had it under his pillow.

Slowly, Frank Salgo approached the bed and stood over the sleeping pair. A wave of nausea passed over him, followed by a chill that made his teeth chatter. He'd have to kill Petrus, he thought. He really had no choice. As for his mother, he'd get the money and be gone before she even woke to realize what had happened. First though, he'd make sure the money was where he thought it was. Letting the knife slide out of his sleeve and into his right hand, he held it over the sleeping man's exposed throat and probed under the pillow with the other. He couldn't feel a thing. He bent down to feel around the edges, reaching farther and farther. Frustration, anger, desire, disbelief. It had to be there. *The money had to be there.* He switched the knife to his left hand so he could reach over his stepfather's head.

A leg shot out from under the sheet; a foot smashed into Frank Salgo's stomach and sent him staggering back against the bureau. Homer Petrus sat up and swung his sturdy legs over the side, outrage making every sinew bulge. But before he could stand up, Frank recovered and, knife clenched tightly, hurled himself at the bigger, stronger man. Half turning, Petrus managed to take the blow in the upper arm instead of the chest. The youth gasped in frustration and pulled the knife out. Blood gushed and spurted on the bed and the sleeping woman.

Magda Petrus awoke, saw a shadowy figure and the glint of steel, felt the warm liquid on her bare flesh. She smelled it and knew what it was. She screamed.

The wounded man felt no pain, a sting, no more, for the moment. He saw the knife upraised a second time, and grabbing his stepson's thin wrist, he twisted till the knife fell to the floor and Frank Salgo screeched with agony.

"I figured it was you," Petrus grunted. "Turn on the light," he told his wife.

Magda Petrus obeyed. "Oh, God, Frank . . ." she moaned. "What have you done?"

"Call the police," her husband ordered.

"No, Homer, no . . ."

"He tried to kill me. He tried to take my money and kill me."

The woman was shaking. "Why, Frank? Why?"

"Because he's no good, that's why!" Petrus shouted. "Because he's too lazy to go to work and earn his way. . ." The flow of blood increased, its sweet sickly odor filling the hot, airless room. Petrus was beginning to feel weak. "Get the police. . ." It was more plea than command.

"You need a doctor. Here, lie down." Gently, Magda Petrus pushed her husband back down on the bed. Ripping part of the sheet, she folded it and pressed it hard against the wound to stanch the flow. "Hold it," she told him. Then, reaching out for the bedside phone, she hissed over her shoulder, "Go, go. Out, get out now. Quick."

Frank Salgo grabbed the few dollars from his stepfather's wallet and ran.

Rather than stand exposed on the platform waiting for a train that might take twenty minutes to come—and still be there when the police answered his mother's call—Frank set out to walk across the Queensboro Bridge into Manhattan. He found a bar on First Avenue that wasn't fussy about serving minors and spent the money he'd taken out of his stepfather's wallet getting drunk. At four A.M. the bar closed and they threw him out along with a couple of diehards. He stumbled downtown. He got as far as Tudor City park. The night was mild and he wasn't afraid to spend what was left of it on a bench. If anybody tried to roll him, all his money was gone anyway; if they tried to hurt him, they'd be sorry—he still had his knife.

Salgo woke stiff and hungry to a dark morning and the threat of rain. He remembered he didn't have enough money to buy breakfast. He thought of going home, sneaking in while his stepfather was in the wholesale market buying for the restaurant. But Homer Petrus wouldn't be getting up early this morning. He wouldn't be going out, probably not for several days. So Frank couldn't go home. There had to be some kind of shelter or soup kitchen nearby, he thought; he was leery about asking a cop. He watched the stream of office workers hurrying to their jobs. Some walked, some rode bicycles, some tried to hail cabs. He chose a woman in her late twenties, dressed in a neat maroon business suit and riding a bicycle. When the traffic light stopped her at the corner, he approached. She was plain, and he gave her his best smile. She not only directed him to an armory a few blocks uptown, but gave him five dollars.

It had been easy. Frank Salgo panhandled for a week and then went home. Petrus slammed the door in his face. He could hear his mother entreating, but she didn't come out after him.

Salgo became unkempt and dirty; his breath foul. The young women he accosted were afraid of him. No one gave him money anymore. He was a marginal being, moving with the bag people. Like them, he gave up the shelters—under the guise of sympathy and compassion there were too many questions, too much earnest effort at rehabilitation. Like them, Frank slept in doorways, in bus and rail terminals, under bridges. Unlike them, he continued to try to panhandle for food and for the booze that made it possible to bear his condition.

At age seventeen, Frank Salgo was stumbling along Times Square with the prostitutes and the pimps, with the forty-, fifty-, and sixty-year-old bums. In a sporadic sweep of the area ordered by the mayor to reassure would-be tourists, Frank was picked up and thrown into the drunk tank.

By comparison, the time spent at Spofford had been a

vacation, a term at a permissive boys' boarding school. There he had been a leader. He bullied the younger boys and they took it. Here, in adult jail, he was at the bottom of the caste system. Weak from long exposure and deprivation, Frank couldn't fight back. He cowered under the abuse. The constant threat of violence and violation were finally the electric shock treatment that galvanized him into a semblance of sanity. He swore to himself that it would never happen again. He would show them all: the cops, his stepfather, and most particularly his mother. On release he immediately looked for work and got a job as a dishwasher. From that he progressed to delivery boy for a supermarket, then to janitor's assistant in a big apartment building, but that consisted mainly of hauling out rich people's garbage. Their scraps were better than the food he ate. He found himself sorting through what they had thrown out and taking home things he couldn't afford to buy.

Rage filled him.

He went back to the knife.

Cautiously, Salgo started mugging sleeping winos, his former streetmates. The most he could get off them was a few bucks, if that. So he moved on to the feeble elderly. Within a month he had found a more affluent set of victims and established a working pattern. He cased the many small, elegant townhouses on the East Side that had no doorman. He gained admittance simply by ringing someone's bell and murmuring: *Delivery, ma'am*. If he got in, fine; if not, he tried somewhere else. Sometimes he pushed into the elevator after a victim. Other times, he waited in the lobby till someone came in and then pushed into the apartment behind him or attacked in the hall. Always, he drew blood. Cutting just a little achieved two ends: one, it made the victim very cooperative; two, it gave him a big high. Real big.

Still, he knew he had to do better before he could go home.

Then he met Nancy Hurlock.

Chapter TWO

It was typical July weather: the eighth consecutive day above ninety degrees. Stagnant air hung in a yellow layer of pollution that choked the city. It was a Sunday, and those who could had escaped to the beaches or mountains. Norah Mulcahaney couldn't get away. In the duty rotation, Sergeant Mulcahaney wouldn't be getting a free weekend until after Labor Day. Not that it mattered. Since Joe's death one day was like another. Her husband, Captain Joseph Antony Capretto, had been killed eight months before. He had died violently, gunned down and then run over and dragged through the streets by a pair of thugs he'd interrupted during the course of a rape attempt in a parking lot. The mindless brutality, the fact that the intended victim hadn't come forward to identify her attackers until a reward was offered, had pushed Norah beyond the pain of her loss to the edge of disillusion. The work she had loved and taken pride in performing was a feeble and futile effort to stem a tidal wave of crime. Half the force was either into drugs, alcohol, or corrupt. She had wanted to resign and get out of New York. She had wanted to run away. Inspector James Felix, her boss at the time and an old friend, refused to accept the resignation. Instead, he insisted she take a leave of absence. Norah agreed, but she'd had no intention of returning.

But she did come back. It had taken only two months as a

civilian for Norah to learn that police work was an integral part of her life. The trick, Joe had told her over and over, was not to get personally involved, but Norah knew now that, for her, absolute detachment couldn't work. She couldn't stop caring. If that got in the way of her private life, then whoever was around would have to put up with it.

Norah was assigned to head a task force whose purpose was to stop crimes against the religious. Priests, rabbis, ministers were being robbed and assaulted on the streets and in their rectories, churches, and synagogues; nuns were being raped and murdered in and out of their convents. At first rare, the attacks had grown in frequency and brutality. For once, the public did not become case hardened—the shock and outrage was as great at the tenth violation as the first. Norah regarded that as an indication that public apathy was slowly lifting.

Norah and her team attacked the crimes against the religious from several angles. The assaults were usually hit and run, so the first step was to gain the trust and then the cooperation of the neighborhoods where crimes had been committed. Once assured the police cared and were really trying to protect them, the citizens often came forward with information that led to the apprehension of the criminal. A sense of inter-reliance was established, and Norah could only hope that it would last after individual cases were cleared and the team moved on.

Decoys were also used—officers dressed as priests or nuns or rabbis. When they turned out *not* to be so helpless and were backed up by plainclothes cops, the word spread that attacking the religious was getting risky. The number of assaults diminished. After four months the task force was disbanded, quietly and with no publicity so potential perpetrators would not be tempted to start again.

Sergeant Norah Mulcahaney (she had always used her maiden name on the job) went back to her regular work on Homicide, Fourth Zone, with a sense of accomplishment that made up for a lot of past failures and frustrations. Joe would have been pleased, she thought. And though the loneliness wasn't eased, it became a bit more bearable.

Norah had been content with her rank. Having observed both her husband and Jim Felix become relegated to administrative work in their parallel advance, she had thought she would remain a sergeant for the rest of her career. As a sergeant, she had the best of both worlds, Norah reasoned. She retained a personal contact with the public and added to it enough authority, if not to direct, then at least to steer an investigation. Now she admitted that even from behind a desk neither Captain Joseph Capretto nor Inspector James Felix had lost touch with the reality of police work. They had remained as sensitive as ever to the problems of the street, to the concerns of the ordinary cop, and to the ever-growing fears of the public. And they had better opportunity to do something about it. So, quietly, without telling anyone, Norah began to prepare for the lieutenant's exam.

And about time too, she thought as she returned the manual to her locker: she was thirty-six, a ten-year veteran. God, ten years! *A veteran!* Did she look thirty-six she wondered as she gazed into the mirror on the back of the door. She didn't feel it. She certainly didn't feel like a veteran. Norah was tall, five foot nine. Her dark brown hair, which she was currently wearing long again and tied back, was healthy and lustrous, her skin white and clear, enhancing the size and depth of her dark blue eyes. Her features were finely chiseled, and she would have been beautiful but for her square blunt jaw. That jaw dominated Norah's face; yet it was what gave it individuality and character. It was the barometer of her mood. At the moment, as she smiled in anticipation, it was almost soft.

Norah Mulcahaney closed the locker, walked down the stairs and out of the Eighty-second Street station house. By the time she'd gone the two blocks to where she'd parked her car on Central Park West, she was dragging. The dress she had chosen for Toni's reception was a pale beige voile with full skirt and full sleeves. It looked, and was, cool.

Unfortunately, the waist was a little snug and the wide turquoise belt much too tight. She hadn't worn the thing since
last summer and hadn't tried it on after it came back from
the cleaner's. It must have shrunk. Norah pursed her lips
ruefully: it hadn't shrunk, she had spread. She should either
go on a diet or buy a new wardrobe.

The heat inside the closed car was like a sauna, but since
the drive across the park to the East Side was too short for
the air conditioning to take effect, Norah didn't bother to
turn it on. By the time she reached Fifth Avenue, she was
soaked with sweat. Then she couldn't find a parking space
and it was too late to turn the air conditioning on. By the
time she found a space, way over on Second, she didn't care.
The long walk back to Lexington in high-heeled, open sandals was hard on her feet and her temper. If she had left the
car and taken a taxi, she would have arrived cool and pres-
entable. Instead, she entered the small enclosed courtyard
of the Sheridan Gallery limping, disheveled, and out of
sorts.

The air conditioning brought goose bumps of relief. Now,
if only she could find a place to fix herself up . . . She was
handed a glass of white wine and a photocopied catalogue.

"So glad you could come."

The hostess said it automatically. Hiding under a mask of
makeup, her shape camouflaged by a black silk caftan encrusted with gold embroidery, she moved on before Norah
had a chance to ask the way to the ladies' room.

Making her way through the elegant, indolent crowd, the
first thing that struck Norah was the professionalism of the
paintings displayed against the white walls. This was, after
all, the work of young people, students. The gallery was a
prestigious one. The Sheridan, located on East Sixty-fifth—
on the very same block where Richard Nixon had bought a
town house, since resold—occupied its own four-story building, and Norah had expected that the students' exhibition
would be off in a back room somewhere. Apparently, it took
up the entire premises. She was not prepared for the number

and stylishness of the guests. She had anticipated no more than parents and relatives, with a scattering of friends.

Glass and catalogue in hand, Norah moved dutifully from painting to painting, allotting each one the same impartial amount of time while inside she was chafing to get to Toni's work. According to the list Antonia DeVecchi, her dear niece, had three pieces on display, numbers twenty-five, sixty-two, and sixty-five. The first should be on the ground floor. As she approached the room where she would surely find the first of Toni's works, Norah spent less and less time over that of the others. At last she reached what she was looking for and was, again, unprepared. And disappointed. She had expected more. Or maybe less. What she saw was a medley of green blobs ranging from acid yellow to a deep blue bordering on bluish-purple. What was it meant to be? A forest? Norah glanced at the small title plaque on the corner of the frame: "Springtime." Why not? It could be whatever the viewer wished. She saw evidence of a certain technical skill in the blending of the hues, and a schoolgirl neatness in application. Well, Toni was a schoolgirl. Norah frowned. Toni could draw; she was good at still life, meticulous with detail, could even do witty caricatures. Why was her niece, a sweet and sensible girl, ignoring her true talent? Leaving the rest of the exhibits behind, Norah headed for the stairs to the second floor and Toni's other two paintings.

She came immediately to number sixty-two, hanging on her left. This one was done in the same basic style and technique as the other, seemingly abstract but representational on closer examination. At first, one was aware only of blended colors, blues this time. Then they took form and became a pool in a forest, its water open to a limpid sky. Pretty, romantic—until one noticed the concentric circles in the water from which a slim white arm reached up, the fingers of the hand outstretched. The hand of someone drowning, grasping for help. Every throbbing vein and sinew delineated. The incongruity of the romantic setting and the gruesome detail of that arm and hand disturbed Norah.

What inside Antonia DeVecchi, a girl of fifteen, had caused her to produce it?

Unfortunately, Norah knew the answer. Or thought she did.

At age twelve, Antonia DeVecchi had been raped with a Coke bottle by a gang of girls in the school washroom. Comforted by the love of her parents and family, the child made a quick recovery, suffered neither permanent physical nor psychic injury. The family hoped and believed that Toni had forgotten. What had stirred the child's subconscious? The painting bespoke violence in the midst of serenity. Norah sought number sixty-five.

It was even more disturbing. The colors were shaded from pale rose to crimson. The central episode, an immolation or transfiguration. The figure in the flames was a woman, her face without features. She was consumed and at the same time drawn up and freed by an unseen power. At the touch on her arm, Norah jumped. Toni smiled shyly.

As was the way with Latin girls, Toni was maturing early. Her bosom was full, her hips sensuous. With her oval face framed by masses of dark curly hair and her dark eyes, she resembled her mother, Lena, the eldest of Joe's seven sisters and the most beautiful. From her father, Giaccomo "Jake" DeVecchi, the child inherited a strength and courage not readily discernible through her shyness. Dressed in a white silk blouse and ballerina-length flowered skirt, Toni DeVecchi looked very grown up and excited. As she linked arms with Norah, her whole being glowed.

"What do you think? Do you like it?"

"To be honest, darling, I don't understand it."

"Oh." The girl's face fell. "It's supposed to—"

"No. Never explain." A man had come up to them and interrupted. "You must let your work stand on its own without apology."

The admonition didn't upset Toni. On the contrary, she looked up eagerly and raised her face for the stranger to kiss. Everybody kissed everybody nowadays, Norah told herself; it was the ordinary social greeting. The man, who had first chided Toni and was now kissing her, was tall, thin, with red-blond hair that reached the nape of his neck. He had a heavy but neatly trimmed beard. His eyes were small, amber-colored, and gleamed brightly from beneath thick brows. His nose was straight and his lips full. With all that facial hair it was hard to judge his age—say late thirties or early forties. It was not so much his kissing her niece that bothered Norah as the way Toni received the kiss.

"There's no title on the work," Norah pointed to the corner of the frame.

"This is my art instructor, Adrian Gourdine. Adrian, this is my aunt, Norah." Toni was radiant again, her eyes on the teacher.

"You didn't tell me you had such an attractive aunt, Antonia. I'm delighted to meet you, Miss. . . ?"

"Mrs. Capretto."

"Mrs. Capretto." Bowing slightly in acknowledgment, Gourdine managed to suggest amusement that she had stressed the title. "I hope you and your husband are enjoying the exhibit."

"I'm a widow."

"I'm sorry."

Standard exchange, yet he was making Norah feel awkward. "Toni has talked so much about you, Mr. Gourdine," Norah told him, very much in the tone of an aunt. She knew Gourdine taught art at Toni's school, that he was an artist himself—a sculptor? And that he held classes in his loft-studio for special pupils who showed talent. "She says you're a fine teacher." Norah waved her hand vaguely to include the various paintings. "This is certainly a very impressive body of work. Was it all done during the spring term?"

"Most of it."

"You have some gifted students. And," she added, "obviously, they have an excellent teacher."

"Thank you." Adrian Gourdine smiled and put his hand lightly on Toni's shoulder. "This is my prize pupil."

"Really?" Norah was interested only in Toni's reaction. "Surely you agree?"

He'd put her on the spot. She didn't like him, Norah decided. His charm was too patently practiced, but Toni was entranced. "No one thinks more of Toni and of all her talents than I do."

"Of course, she has a great deal to learn."

"I'm to have private lessons this fall," Toni offered eagerly."

"Is that so?"

"Mom and Dad said okay, so it's settled." Toni continued to glow. Norah frowned.

"Antonia, I would like to speak to your aunt privately. Will you excuse us for a few moments?"

The girl bit her lip and looked from one to the other before she turned and made her way through the groups of visitors out to the back and a small open terrace.

Gourdine waited till she was out of earshot. "It's quite apparent that you disapprove of Antonia's continuing her art lessons, Mrs. Capretto. Is it because you don't understand her work? I don't think you recognize the extent of Antonia's promise."

"Oh, I think I do, Mr. Gourdine." Toni was the daughter Norah had never had and probably never would have. She cared deeply for her and the girl returned the love. So maybe she was taking it all too seriously, but she didn't like the art teacher's reaction. "Toni has a knack, a facility for drawing. She has the precision almost of a draftsman, but you're not letting her use it, much less develop it. It sneaks into her work and it's the only good thing there." She pointed. "The arm and hand in that blue one—the detail is impressive."

"Copied out of an anatomy book."

"What's wrong with that? Leonardo da Vinci's notebooks are filled with drawings of parts of the anatomy."

"Evidently you don't like modern art."

"Mr. Gourdine, it's quite obvious that Toni has a crush on

you. The paintings are a romantic celebration of her feelings on the one hand and her fear of where they may lead on the other."

"A schoolgirl crush. There's nothing unusual or terrible about that."

Norah, of course, was not referring to a young girl's normal sexual apprehensions, but to Toni's very special trauma. He couldn't know that, she realized. "I'd rather you didn't encourage the child's feeling for you."

"I'm encouraging her talent."

"What other students are you encouraging?"

"I hope I encourage all my students." His amber eyes crinkled at the corners and he smiled. "Why don't you like me, Mrs. Capretto? What have I done to cause you displeasure?"

Norah hesitated. She liked most people. At worst, she remained neutral. She knew she tended to be overprotective of Toni; still, it didn't explain her resentment of this man. Briefly, she considered explaining to Adrian Gourdine the dreadful shock her niece had experienced and her precarious emotional balance, but her instinct was not to trust him—in effect, not to give him knowledge he might use unscrupulously.

"I neither like nor dislike you, Mr. Gourdine. I don't know you well enough."

"We can do something about that." He smiled. He took a step closer. They almost touched. Despite the milling crowd and constant flow of chatter all around, he made Norah feel as though they were alone.

As his pale amber eyes looked into hers, then traveled down to her mouth, Norah flushed. Air conditioning notwithstanding, she was as hot and uncomfortable as she had been racing along the street. She knew she looked flustered; she remembered she hadn't had a chance to fix herself up when she arrived, that her hair must be a mess and her makeup melted into a disaster. So the play he was making was a fake all the way.

"We could have dinner," he suggested. "This will be over about six." He pointed to the dregs in Norah's glass. "Let me buy you a decent drink and then dinner."

"I'm busy tonight. Thank you."

"Tomorrow night then."

"I'll be busy tomorrow too."

"I see."

"I'm asking you to be honest with Toni about her ability and her potential." Norah looked directly at him and spoke earnestly.

"In other words, you don't want me to take her on as a pupil this fall."

"That's right."

Adrian Gourdine paused. It was evident he was deciding just what tone to take. "As long as Antonia wants to come and her parents permit, there's nothing you can do about it."

Norah responded to the challenge instantly; her chin went up. "I wouldn't count on that, Mr. Gourdine."

Chapter
THREE

Inga Larsen's alarm went off at five-fifteen A.M. She responded instantly, almost bounding out of bed. It was still dark, but she was used to that. She reveled in being awake and active when most others slept. Inga turned on the light beside the bed, then the one in the bathroom. While brushing her teeth she heard the click of the automatic timer followed by the sound of coffee perking in the kitchen. The good rich smell pervaded the tiny studio apartment. She gave her face a quick splash of cold water—the shower would come after her run—and returned to her bedroom to dress.

Inga Larsen was petite but full-bodied. Her skin was white and rosy; her hair, pale as platinum, was cut in bangs across her forehead and hung straight and shining down her back. By the time she had laced up her jogging shoes, the coffee was ready. She took a cup. A full breakfast would also come after the workout.

Inga walked into the hall, rang for the elevator, and then emerged into the silent street just as light was breaking.

She wasn't afraid. There were other silent figures, runners like her, getting in their stint before going to work. Inga lived just off Central Park West, a short half block from the Seventy-second Street entrance to the park. She took the footpath down to the lake, turning east. Some liked to run along the transverse, then follow the East Drive, using the road all the way, but Inga enjoyed jogging along the foot-paths; it gave her the greater illusion that she was actually out in the country. Either way, there were many choices along the route. Since Inga particularly liked to be near the water, she started along the transverse but left it at Cherry Hill. From there she intended to go down a grassy slope to the edge of the lake, but she hesitated. There had been no rain in over two weeks and the lake was drying up; only slimy, stagnant pools were left. Nevertheless, Inga decided to take her regular course. If she changed, she might not *accidentally* run into Paul Coates.

Bands of electric blue and orange rimmed the horizon as the blonde started down the hill. Before she reached the bottom, she spotted the woman lying prone across the cement path just short of the Bow Bridge. She stopped. The woman didn't move. Had she fallen? She was lying on her stomach, right arm stretched out, right leg half bent under her. Inga Larsen looked around. She was alone. It was very still. No sound of traffic or of people or even the chirping of birds. At this hour there should have been other joggers. Where were they? *Oh, God, where was everybody? Where was Paul?* She took a couple of tentative steps toward the woman.

"Hello?" she called out. "Hello?"

There was no answer, not so much as a twitch of movement.

Inga Larsen bent forward for a closer look. She screamed. Then she turned and ran.

Though Norah hurried, she found most of the regulars already on the scene. Patrol cars from the Central Park precinct predominated but there were also units from her own Two-Oh parked at the fountain at the top of the hill, plus the usual complement of unmarked police cars. The morgue wagon and the assistant medical examiner's BMW were parked down below right at the lake edge. The fingerprints and photo vans were down there too.

Norah had been here before. Homicides in the park were

all too ordinary and this, unfortunately, was one of the preferred locations. In spite of her familiarity with the area, she
paused for a moment to look from her high vantage point. It
should have been a serene vista. There was not a sigh of a
breeze. A milky haze hung over the metallic waters. The
carefully irregular shoreline dotted with pergolas and cunningly planted willows seemed painted in lacquer. Above,
through the layers of grime, the sun's red ball was an omi-
nous sign that the oppressive heat would continue. For now
at least, it was still cool.

The huddle of detectives and technicians indicated where
the body was. Norah spotted Ferdi Arenas at the edge of the
group just as he looked up and caught sight of her. She
indicated she would come down, but the direct way across
the grass was roped off, protecting a section of terrain that
looked as though something heavy had been dragged over it.
The grass was crushed and stained, marking a dark viscous
trail. Inside the roped area were a woman's purse and an
overturned picnic basket, its contents partially scattered.
Ferdi, a young and ambitious detective who had gone back
into uniform in order to make sergeant, was the one who
had acted to preserve the evidence, Norah was certain. Although he'd passed the sergeant's exam high on the list and
gained appointment, Arenas unfortunately had not been re-
assigned to the detectives—that was the risk one took. But
he soon would be, Norah hoped. Chief Deland could not
continue to overlook him.

"Hi," Norah greeted as they met halfway. "Did you get an
ID?"

There was a close bond between the two, which neither
openly admitted. Arenas was ten years younger but he
didn't look it. The lines of tragedy were already deeply
etched on his face; the dark hair prematurely gray. While
serving on the pilot Senior Citizens Squad headed by Norah,
Arenas had been backup when the team's decoy was killed.
The decoy had been Officer Pilar Nieves, his fiancée. There
was nothing he could have done to stop it. It had been no
accident but a shrewdly worked out plan, the hunted baiting

the trap for the hunter. He knew all that—but he couldn't forget. No more than Norah could forget how Joe had died, or shake her sense of responsibility.

Ferdi nodded in answer to Norah's question. "There was a driver's license in her purse and a social security card. Her name is Nancy Hurlock. She lives in Great Neck and works in Manhattan at the Metropolitan Bank on Forty-fourth and Lex."

"How did she die?"

"Her throat was cut."

Noting that the forensic and technical people were still working around the body, Norah decided to take a closer look around the scene before joining them. Motioning for Arenas to go with her, she stepped over the rope and made her way down to a small plateau dominated by an ancient, gnarled cherry tree, its limbs spread wide forming a natural canopy. It shielded them from the sight of anyone above. From below they were screened by a tangled euonymus hedge. Judging by the trail of blood, this was where the victim had been cut and then dragged down to the lake. But why? Why would the killer drag her out of concealment and leave her on the path where anyone might stumble over her?

"Anything else in her purse?" Norah asked.

"Her car keys. Her car was parked on the rotunda overnight." Ferdi pointed up to the fountain area where Norah and the other officers had left their cars. "The park patrol put a ticket on it."

"So." She didn't need to ask whether he'd requested a tow truck to haul the victim's car to the police garage. There it would be checked for fingerprints, blood, hair, fabric threads—everything and anything. "Who found the body?"

"A jogger. Miss Inga Larsen." Arenas indicated the girl sitting on a bench to their left along the lake path, some distance from the Bow Bridge.

"Anything useful?"

"No, but I didn't push. She's very upset. Almost hysterical."

"Okay. I'll give it a try."

As she approached, Norah observed the witness. The lines of her body were youthful; her legs well shaped, the thighs firm, muscled, and tanned. Her face was hidden by a long silky sweep of silver-blonde hair. She was hunched in on herself; her posture suggested deep distress.

"Miss Larsen? I'm Sergeant Mulcahaney. May I sit down?"

The girl looked up. The sweat from the exercise had long since dried; tears ran down her cheeks instead. "I don't know anything. Couldn't I please go home?"

"I just want to ask you one or two questions, Miss Larsen, then you can go," Norah replied soothingly.

The soft gray eyes were streaked with red. "I don't know anything!" she exclaimed. "I told the officers. I told the sergeant. How many times do I have to say it? I don't know anything. I never saw the woman before in my life."

Norah sat down on the bench, close but not touching. "What time was it when you discovered her?"

"I'm not sure. A little after six. I already explained . . ." She looked around to find the particular person to whom she'd given that particular bit of information, then gave up. She sighed heavily. "I left my apartment at six like I do every morning. It never takes me more than ten minutes to get to this point—I live just off Central Park West. I took my usual route. I did consider going another way . . ." Her voice trailed off. She sighed again; in that sigh was the thought of what she would have been spared. "Anyhow, I came down that path, and I saw a woman lying at the bottom of the hill. I thought, well, I thought somebody had mugged her; that's what I thought. I was frightened. I was afraid that he might still be around, hiding. That's why I ran. I was scared."

"Was there anyone around?"

"I don't know. I didn't look."

"Of course not."

"I ran away." Inga Larsen shook her blonde head. "I should have stayed. I should have stayed, but I ran. I saw the blood and, God forgive me, I ran." Fresh tears ran over the old.

"You did call the police," Norah consoled.

The girl went on crying softly.

"Don't take it so hard, Miss Larsen, there are some who wouldn't even have done that much."

"That's not the point. Don't you see? I might have been able to help. I don't know. I'll never know. I might have been able to help her . . ." Her pretty face was twisted with despair. "I'm a nurse."

Norah put out a hand and rested it on the blonde's shoulder. "From the amount of blood I saw up there on the hill, you were much too late no matter what you might have tried."

"Do you really think so?" The gray eyes were wide and appealing.

Norah answered without hesitation, "Yes, I do. I'm sure that you made an instinctive evaluation that was professional and did the only thing that you could do by calling the police."

"Thank you." Inga Larsen relaxed. "Can I go home now?"

"Unless there's something more you can tell me."

"No. I'm sorry. I wish there were. Oh, God, I really wish there were."

It was good enough for Norah. She turned and finally headed for a look at the victim.

Nancy Hurlock was lying on the path, head and right arm resting on the pavement, lower body and legs on the edge of the grass. Norah couldn't see her face because Doc Worgan was kneeling and obstructing her view, but the figure was slight. She wore a white dress splashed with red poppies, their color still vivid though the splotches of blood had turned dark. She wore white, open-toed pumps. Her legs were bare but hardly tanned.

Phillip Worgan got up and stepped aside.

Norah gasped aloud. She couldn't help herself. No wonder Inga Larsen, though she was a nurse, had run away. The neck and shoulders of the victim were covered with blood. A lot of it, of course, had been spilled at the top of the hill or it would have been worse. Norah swallowed hard and forced herself to look at what was almost a black gash straight across the delicate white neck. Her stomach heaved and for a couple of seconds she thought she was going to throw up. Sure, she'd seen as bad before and often enough to get used to it, but she never did; and she was finally resigned that she never would. She wondered how doctors managed. It was a relief to raise her eyes to the victim's face. Nancy Hurlock was neither pretty nor plain—undistinguished, but she did have a touching elfin quality. Her brown eyes were wide open with the look that sudden death so often left imprinted—surprise. She was young, not much over twenty.

"The knife was sharp and he was strong. He needed only one cut," Phillip Worgan told her. He paused. "What's interesting is that the cut is straight rather than curved. It indicates he attacked while facing her."

In the three years since Worgan had joined the New York Medical Examiner's Office, Norah had encountered him on many cases, but she had never known him to volunteer information at the crime scene. Worgan came from Syracuse, where he'd been chief medical officer, and had brought with him both his expertise and the habit of command. The latter had not been well received. Just under five foot eight, chunky, with thick brown hair and small brown eyes that pointed inquisitively from behind steel-rimmed glasses, he was, at thirty-two, stooped by the demands he made on himself. Worgan was a loner neither attracting nor seeking friends. He had come to work under Asa Osterman to learn his methods and because of Dr. Osterman's reputation as a forensic scientist. Also, of course, knowing that Osterman was already many years over retirement age, Worgan wanted to be in line for the job. He was dismayed, therefore, that he was not respectfully welcomed but barely tolerated. He had come as an expert among experts and found himself a beginner in a field he had hitherto ignored—dealing with people. Here, he was one of a team. To do the kind of analysis that he considered within the purview of a medical examiner—a rounded picture of the medical, psychological, and factual aspects of a crime—it wasn't enough to bark an order. He needed the good will of all criminal justice personnel. He had to ask for cooperation. It didn't come easy, but he worked on it.

He felt a particular warmth for Sergeant Mulcahaney because she had treated him in a friendly manner right from the start. "There's no evidence of sexual abuse," he continued in his new manner. "Of course, we can't be sure till we do the autopsy."

Norah nodded. "You say he attacked her from the front. She wouldn't have stood still. Apparently, she didn't." She pointed to the trail of blood.

"I was just coming to that," Worgan snapped. For all his new affability he still didn't like anyone, particularly a non-medical person, to anticipate his reasoning. He pursed his lips, then sighed and managed a smile. "You should have been a pathologist, Sergeant. Let's go on up."

Norah waved to Arenas and the three of them walked to the base of the cherry tree.

"He did it here." Worgan pointed to the large dark path of grass Norah had already noted.

"Right." Careful where she stepped, Norah moved around the enclosed area once more. She examined the contents spilled from the picnic basket. There was a packet of sandwiches—thick slices of ham and cheese on dark bread still sealed; two hard-boiled eggs, shells not so much as cracked; a container of cole slaw, unopened; a quarter section of chocolate cake in Saran wrap; two fresh peaches; a six-pack of Miller Lite, intact.

"There's just enough for two," Arenas pointed out. "She wouldn't have gone to all this trouble for a girlfriend. We know that's her car up there. So, she and her date drove here in her car. On the way over they got into an argument. They arrived, parked, got out, still arguing. On the way down, he attacked her. The hamper was either dropped or knocked over."

Norah shook her head. "I don't think so. This place is secluded, but only to a point. Last night was real hot. There must have been fifty people out here looking for relief."

"It could have happened after dark when everybody was gone."

"Why would they have waited so late to eat?" Norah argued. "Have the photographers finished?" she asked and at Worgan's nod bent down and turned the basket upright and looked inside. She founded a folded cloth, took it out and spread it. "Look at the grass stains and the dirt. I think this cloth was laid out, then picked up again, refolded, and put away. I think Nancy Hurlock arrived here first and waited for her date. She would have had to get here early to secure this preferred spot. While she waited, she unpacked and spread out the meal."

"But he didn't show," Arenas picked up. "She waited till it was dark and gave up; packed the stuff away and started back up the hill to her car."

There was a pause while the three visualized the scene.

"And then a stranger, a mugger, attacked her?" Worgan wondered aloud.

"That's a lot of blood spilled for a casual assault," Arenas murmured. "Maybe her date finally did show up. He met her coming down."

Norah nodded. "He stood slightly above her, and as she tilted her head back for his kiss, he cut her." Anger and repulsion welled up inside her.

"It could have happened like that," Worgan agreed, returning to his brisk manner. "It was an awkward position and maybe that's why he did such a sloppy job and why she survived as long as she did. Naturally, she couldn't speak, much less call for help. She didn't have the strength to pull herself up to the parking area, so instead she crawled down to the open path hoping that someone would come by and find her."

Someone should have found her, Norah thought. With all the people out searching for a breath of air on that hot night, someone should have come across Nancy Hurlock as she lay dying. But nobody had had Nurse Larsen's decency and called in.

FOUR

The Hurlocks had reported their daughter missing on Sunday night. They were told, routinely, that as an adult she might be away by her own choice. No protestation that Nancy had never in her life stayed out till two in the morning, no pleading availed. The desk sergeant was sympathetic but firm. He did assure the parents that accident and hospital reports would be checked, and they would be notified if anything developed. Otherwise, call back in twenty-four hours.

The Hurlocks contacted all of Nancy's friends. She didn't have many and none of them were close. She was not a girl who liked to chatter and giggle. She was shy, withdrawn, had never had a steady boyfriend. Nevertheless, Jeffrey Hurlock called everyone his wife Roseanne could think of. No one had any idea where Nancy might be. At four A.M. Jeffrey Hurlock got into his Cadillac Seville and drove around the neighborhood looking. She might have been attacked on her way home. She might have had an accident, might be lying somewhere . . . At six A.M. he was back—alone.

They didn't know what else to do.

They were an elderly couple. Nancy was their only child, the daughter of their mature years and thus doubly dear. By the time Norah Mulcahaney arrived at the door of their four-bedroom brick Colonial set back in a wooded acre on a dead-end lane, Jeffrey and Roseanne were sitting together in a trance, waiting for the telephone to ring—and fearful that it would.

The ring of the doorbell sent a shock through both of them. The husband went to answer while the wife watched in dread from the middle of the living room.

"Yes?" Hurlock stared at a woman he had never seen before.

"Mr. Hurlock?" Norah opened her ID wallet for him to see. "I'm Sergeant Mulcahaney. I'd like to talk to you."

"Sergeant . . . Oh, yes, yes, please, please come in. They told me . . . us . . . last night, uh . . . this morning, nothing could be done for twenty-four hours. We're so grateful that you came over. We really appreciate . . . we've been so worried. Please, please come in."

He was a tall, good-looking man in his late fifties, with a tan acquired while sailing during the summer and maintained year-round at a tanning center. It set off the halo of frost-white hair and the dark bushy eyebrows. He kept himself fit physically and mentally. He was, in fact, a $70,000-a-year executive for the Mercury Courier Service. In one sleepless night, the years he had held at bay had penetrated his defenses.

"Honey, this is Sergeant Mulcahaney. My wife, Roseanne." Even his deep resonant voice was raspy.

Mrs. Hurlock was plump, her dark hair streaked blonde. She had a round face whose youthful contour was spoiled by deep lines and sagging jowls. Of the two, she had the greater courage; she went straight to the point.

"Have you found her? Have you found Nancy? Is she all right?"

There was only one way; Norah knew that. In all the times she'd faced anxious parents, lovers, and friends, she had found no other easier either for them or for herself.

"I'm sorry. Nancy's dead."

There was a moment of stunned silence, then Roseanne Hurlock began to cry softly. Quietly, she let the tears course down her cheeks, running into the deep channels at her nose and mouth.

Her husband refused to accept it. "They told us they couldn't do anything till she'd been missing for twenty-four hours. The last time we saw her was six last night. That's not twenty-four hours so they couldn't have even started looking for her yet."

"I'm not from your local station," Norah explained. "I'm from Manhattan. Homicide division."

"Oh, my God!" the mother gasped and turned her face to the wall. Though her sobbing was silent, it racked her whole body.

"Nancy was found early this morning in Central Park," Norah told them.

Somehow, Mrs. Hurlock managed to speak though she didn't turn around. "She was going for a picnic. She took food out of the refrigerator and packed a basket."

"Why should she go to Central Park for a picnic, for God's sake!" the father exploded. "She's got real country, real woods and a beach right here. That's why we bought this place, isn't it? So that Nancy, so that all of us, could get away from the stink and the noise . . . Oh, Christ . . ." he groaned. "Why should she do that?" he asked plaintively, but not of his wife nor the officer.

"The other girls didn't have cars and didn't want to take the train to come out here. It was easier for her to go in," Mrs. Hurlock placated.

"What girls? Who was she going with?"

"Girls from the office. She didn't mention their names."

"And you didn't ask? You didn't insist on knowing who they were? You should have told me. I would have found out. Or I wouldn't have let her out of this house. God! *How many times do I have to remind you of what it's like out there?* Nancy's a young, innocent, naive girl. The only way we can protect her is to know who she's with and what she's doing at all times."

Mrs. Hurlock cringed.

"She had no business going to Central Park. That's a dangerous place. People get—" he stopped, appalled.

It was time for Norah to take charge. "I understand Nancy worked in Manhattan."

"Yes," Hurlock replied. "At the Metropolitan Bank near Grand Central."

Both parents were relieved to shift, if only temporarily, to a noncontroversial subject. Both had started to answer at once, but Mrs. Hurlock, as usual, deferred to her husband.

"She . . . was in the corporate service department." The bitterness with which he used the past tense was acknowledgment of his child's death. It made Roseanne Hurlock wince. She took a tentative half step toward him, started to reach, then drew back.

"I suppose when Nancy didn't return at a reasonable hour, you did call some of her friends," Norah suggested. "Did that include the girls she worked with and was supposed to have gone on the picnic with?"

Neither one of the Hurlocks caught the *supposed*. Dolefully, Mrs. Hurlock shook her head. "We had no idea how to reach them. I only knew their first names: Kate, Helen, Joyce."

"Did Nancy have a boyfriend?"

"No!" Hurlock snapped.

"Did she date? Did she go out with different young men?"

"Living out here and working in the city made it difficult," Mrs. Hurlock seemed embarrassed.

"She didn't date at all?"

Her mother licked her lips. "Nancy wasn't popular," she admitted, and it hurt. Then she blanched in the realization that she too had used the past tense. Her round face twitched and she gushed on compulsively, as her husband had done earlier. "Nancy was very shy. In high school she was a fine swimmer, number one on the team; she was a lovely dancer, but she didn't 'hang out' with any clique. You know how that is. On the night of her senior prom she stayed home."

"She was selective," Hurlock defended.

"The picnic basket was provisioned for two people," Norah told them.

Mrs. Hurlock appeared confused; her husband wary. "So?"

"The contents didn't suggest a group picnic. If she had been meeting a group she would have brought one or two items in quantity." Norah waited for comment, but they were waiting too. "We believe Nancy had a date with a man. The food was not eaten. The cloth had been laid out and then returned to the basket. Perhaps there was a quarrel."

"Was she . . .? Had she been . . ." Hurlock couldn't bring himself to say it.

"No. It appears she was not. We'll know definitely after the autopsy."

"Autopsy!" her mother moaned.

"I'm sorry, Mrs. Hurlock. It has to be done. It's the law and it's necessary."

But Jeffrey Hurlock remained concerned with the possible violation of his daughter's living body. Some color had returned to his face under the heavy tan, he looked less jaundiced. "She died defending herself," he pronounced and drew erect.

There had been no evidence of a struggle on that hillside, but why deny Hurlock the consolation? And it could have happened that way: the killer might have tried to rape Nancy and she resisted. "I think that's all for now," Norah concluded. "Someone will have to come down to identify Nancy. Later. I'll let you know."

They stood in the middle of the pretentious living room with its cathedral ceiling, surrounded by their hard-earned luxuries, and at last reached out to touch each other and share the sorrow. Arms entwined, they forgot the policewoman, and Norah started for the door intending to let herself out. Mrs. Hurlock raised her head from her husband's shoulder.

"Sergeant . . ."

"Yes?"

"How did she die?"

"She was stabbed."

The ravaged face showed little additional pain. Hurlock's frown deepened slightly.

They assumed she had died quickly, Norah realized. Maybe it didn't occur to them that it could have been otherwise. Maybe they were afraid to ask. Why tell them their daughter had crawled on the ground on her belly in a desperately futile attempt to get help? That it had taken her hours to die, long hours through the night? When they went to the morgue to view the body, attendants would make sure the rubber sheet was neatly tucked under the chin to hide the terrible wound. Of course, they would find out ultimately, inevitably. They would read it in the papers; they might even see pictures of the scene, arrows pointing to the long trail of their daughter's blood. If somehow they should be spared, then once the perpetrator was caught it would all come out at the trial. There was no way Norah could prevent it. She could buy them time; by then it might not hurt so much.

It was too soon for the autopsy report. Probably Phil Worgan wouldn't even begin the procedure till the next day: there was always a backlog. For the same reason it was also too soon to expect any news from the lab regarding Nancy Hurlock's car. Nevertheless, after stopping for a Junior Whopper at a Burger King on Queens Boulevard, Norah returned to the squad room. Among the messages on her desk was one from Adrian Gourdine. For a moment, Norah didn't remember. She frowned; then a smile touched the corners of her lips. Sure, Toni's art teacher. And now he knew she was a cop. So he was probably having second thoughts about taking Jake and Lena's money for art lessons their daughter wasn't qualified for. She tossed the paper into the waste basket.

One message she didn't toss aside was from Father Boylan, pastor of the Our Lady of Perpetual Help parish. She held that in her hand and stared at it for a very long time. The two names brought back terrible memories, memories she knew would never fade and still brought pain. She sat down, reached for the telephone and dialed. Father Boylan picked up the phone himself.

"Norah, it's good of you to call back so promptly."

"Of course, Father, as soon as I got your message. What can I do for you?"

"You haven't heard?"

"No."

"We've had a robbery at the church. This morning. It happened some time between the end of the seven A.M. mass and the start of the eight. Someone stole the chalice right off the altar."

"Oh, Father, I'm so sorry."

"It was our finest piece. Our only valuable piece. Solid gold with rubies and diamonds, small rubies and diamonds, but . . ." he sighed.

So did Norah, inwardly. By now the thief had probably sold it for fifty bucks to a fence who would pick out the stones and melt down the vessel to sell the gold by weight. "I assume you notified the precinct?"

"Oh, yes. The detectives came and they were very courteous, but not very concerned. I'm sure they're extremely competent, but I thought since you'd been here before and you know the parish and the people so well . . ."

"Do you know the names of the detectives, Father?"

"Ben Jones and Ed Gregory."

"All right." Norah hesitated. She would give them a call. She was sure that they wouldn't mind if she went over to the church and looked around. She glanced at her watch, nearly three. In these days of budget crisis, overtime was frowned on. Norah didn't want to have to pass the interviewing of the people who had worked with Nancy Hurlock on to another officer. She wanted to handle it herself, to get the feel of the atmosphere around the victim. It wasn't enough to know what was said about Nancy Hurlock; Norah wanted a sense of how the speaker felt about her.

"I can't come over right now, Father, I'm working on a case, but I'll make it as soon as I can."

"I understand, of course. Thank you, Norah."

*   *   *

The bank had closed its doors to the public, but the staff and officers were still there when Norah arrived. She spoke to the branch manager first.

Helene Bach wore the banker's gray version of the recommended uniform for women executives—a severely tailored suit. A spill of white ruffle down the front and at her wrists was a statement repeated in the expertly shaped short and shining crop of chestnut hair and the careful makeup. Her eyes were large and searching. She was young, at the edge of thirty, Norah decided. But it was hard to tell which side; she was sure that Helene Bach would rise a lot higher before she reached forty. Ms. Bach greeted Sergeant Mulcahaney with professional reserve but as an equal, recognizing their respective positions on the ladder of success in a man's field.

She waved Norah to a chair. "I assume you're here about Nancy Hurlock, Sergeant."

The news hadn't been released. "How did you learn of it?"

The branch manager shrugged. "When Nancy didn't come in this morning, we were naturally concerned. She is, she was, a very conscientious worker. If she'd been sick, she would have called in or had someone call in for her."

"So you called her home?"

"Yes."

"I see. What else can you tell me about Nancy?"

"She was shy, plain, kept to herself."

"Did she have any close friends in the bank?"

"She was neither particularly liked nor disliked. Outside, I can't say."

"She told her mother she was going on a picnic in Central Park last evening with some of the women from the bank."

"I don't know anything about that. I consider it unlikely."

"You would have heard if such an outing were being planned?"

"I believe so."

The gleam in those intelligent hazel eyes told Norah there was no way she would have missed.

"How about boyfriends?"

"As I said, I have no knowledge of what she did outside. I never heard her mention a boyfriend. I never saw her with a man."

Helene Bach was forthcoming, but she kept strictly to fact. Norah took a breath. "Do you know how Nancy Hurlock died?"

The manager shook her head.

"Her throat was slashed and she bled to death."

The self-possessed young woman did no more than close her eyes for a moment, but she was shaken.

"I think you know your people very well, Miss Bach," Norah continued. "I think you watch them closely."

"It's part of the job."

"Of course. So you would have noticed any change, any recent change in Nancy Hurlock—in her manner, attitude, mood."

"Yes. In the past month or so she appeared more exhilarated; that's as well as I can describe it. She had a glow; she became almost pretty." The manager frowned, thinking a while longer. "She had never been one to rush home after work, but that changed. She became the first to go out the door at quitting time."

Both knew what that meant—a man.

"But you didn't see her with anyone?" Norah pressed. "Nobody came around to call for her after work?"

"Not as far as I know."

Which was just about definitive, Norah thought. Still . . . "May I talk to the people who worked with her?"

Helene Bach opened both hands outward. "Please." Her lively eyes told Norah it would be a waste of time, but she understood procedure had to be observed.

An hour later Norah was finished with the interviews, and Helene Bach's judgment had indeed been vindicated. None of Nancy's friends, or rather colleagues for she'd had no real friends, had even suspected there might have been a boyfriend, much less seen her with one. Her parents had denied it, Norah pondered. There was no indication of his existence except that overturned picnic basket.

Chapter
FIVE

The trucker reached for May Guttman's hand and held it tight. "How about tonight, honey?"

"Sorry, Howie, I'm busy."

"Tomorrow night?"

"I'm busy tomorrow night too."

"Hell, you're busy every night lately."

"So?" May Guttman raised her carefully plucked eyebrows and pulled loose. She began to clear the table, stacking the dishes on an oval metal tray.

"What's the matter, sweetheart?"

"Nothing's the matter."

"Who is he?"

"Who's who?" The waitress speeded up her work.

"The new man," Howard Baffler replied. "The guy you run out to every night."

May kept her eyes down. "I don't know what you're talking about."

"Don't lie to me!" Baffler shouted, his heavy face flushed, his eyes angry and pleading at the same time.

She didn't answer. Bending, she started to hoist the tray up to her shoulder. As she did, Howie grabbed her elbow to detain her. The dishes went smashing to the ground.

Everybody in the diner—patrons, waitresses, cook, and

counterman—who had been pretending to ignore the argument, jumped. There was a stunned silence.

"Now look what you made me do!" May shouted, between tears and frustration.

She was a pretty girl in her early twenties. Her hair was a
light auburn frizzed in curls all over her head. She had fine
ivory skin and a full sensuous mouth. But the bloom was
fading fast. She was living hard, working and playing ob-
sessively, never still for a moment. It was as though she was
afraid to be alone and confront herself. At seventeen, May
Guttman had run away from home to be with her eighteen-
year-old lover. When she got pregnant, he abandoned her.
She had borne the child, a boy, in a home for unwed mothers, most of them teenagers like herself. After an honest
attempt to support and raise her son, she gave up and
shipped him to Florida to be cared for by her retired parents.
At first, she had gone down regularly to visit him, then less
regularly. The child hardly knew her: the parents offered
only criticism. There was no point.

She had had jobs with more social status than waitressing
but they had paid less. Even more important, at the diner
she met men. She had all the dates she wanted with men of
all ages and varying degrees of constancy, but the one real
love of her life remained the father of her child. She thought
she was looking for someone to make her forget. In truth,
she was searching to replace him.

"God! I'm sorry, May." Howard Baffler got down on his
knees and started distractedly to pick up the broken plates
and gather the spilled food with his hands. At twenty-eight,
he was only five years older than May but he looked forty.
He was a tall, awkward man, walking stoop-shouldered in
the manner he had adopted when he shot up suddenly at
thirteen to become the tallest boy in his class. His neck was
scrawny and he carried his head tilted sideways at an angle
of perpetual apology. But he was no coward. And he was
strong. Howie Baffler had resisted two attempted hijack-

ings. He had sent both pairs of would-be thieves to the hospital while he walked away with an assortment of minor bruises—and the shipment intact. It was emotional stress he couldn't cope with. The quick flushes took a long time to subside; they were the visible indication of dangerously high blood pressure.

Howie wanted to get married. He was making good money and the days of the long haul were behind him. There had been no point marrying when he was on the road all the time. What kind of life would that have been for a woman? His mother had pointed that out to him over and over and, of course, she had been right. But now he was hardly ever away overnight. And his mother had died six months before. If he waited much longer, it would be too late to have children, and Howie wanted children. Looking around for a likely candidate, he fell in love with May.

Baffler knew all about her. He knew about the child; she had made no secret of her son. From Baffler's point of view the boy was an added inducement for them to get married. He was eager to take on the six-year-old as his son. It would be making up for lost time.

"It was my fault, honey, my fault. I'll pay for it. I'll pay for everything." Looking up, Howard Baffler called to the gaunt, raw-boned counterman who was also the night manager. "Hey, Matt! It was my fault. I'll pay. Put it on my tab, okay?"

But May had turned and was running to the employees' rest room. Baffler left the mess on the floor and ran after her only to have the door slammed in his face. He waited for a while, then leaning his cheek against the panel, he murmured humbly.

"May? May, honey, come out, please . . ."

No answer. No sound.

"May! May, you come out! You come out this minute or I'm coming in after you." Baffler pounded on the door with his fists. His color rose to an unhealthy, dangerous scarlet. "Knock it off, May!" he yelled.

The roar of a motor directly behind the diner drowned him out. Not an unusual sound in a shopping center at a crossroad. Ignoring the constriction across his chest and the shooting pain down his left arm, Baffler ran out the door and around the back to the parking section reserved for patrons and employees . . . just in time to see May's '72 Vega hatchback careen out of the lot and merge with traffic on Rockaway Boulevard heading south.

"May . . ." he called helplessly. "Oh, May . . ." he groaned, holding back tears. He watched till her car was out of sight. Head down, heart pounding, and body drenched with sweat, Howie Baffler walked slowly over to his rig. He had one final pickup to make and then he could sign out. He'd pick up his own car and go over to May's place. If she wasn't home, he would wait for her. He would wait all night if necessary.

The call came in to the Mott Avenue Station in Far Rockaway just after eight on Sunday morning. It was made by Henry Nonas, widower and resident in one of the retirement homes along Seagirt Boulevard fronting the ocean. Out for his morning bicycle ride, Mr. Nonas had noticed a car pulled over in one of the lookout spots along the boardwalk. It was not unusual for early morning bathers or fishermen or joggers to leave their cars there. What roused Mr. Nonas's curiosity was that somebody was sitting in the car. It was too early for lovers; anyhow, he could only see one person. For all the beauty of the beach, for all the respectability of the high-rise edifices fronting it and the middle- class community just across the boulevard, Nonas knew the area was ringed by a desolate stretch of dunes, abandoned beach cottages, shacks, and, a few blocks farther on, outright slums. So Henry Nonas pedaled just close enough. What he saw made him brake so hard he nearly fell off his bike.

Detective Gary Reissig of the One-Oh-One caught the squeal. He was a stolid man in his thirties with a stocky, muscular frame, straight blonde hair, and a quiet sense of humor lurking behind tranquil gray eyes. He had been born, raised, and married on the peninsula and was in turn bringing up his own family there. Originally inhabited by the Reuckowacky Indians, the area of the Rockaways and the Five Towns had been rich farmland. The white man gradually took over and continued to farm it until, with the laying of railroad tracks and the construction of the station in Lawrence, contact was established with New York City and people began to build summer homes near the beaches. The area flourished and became a playground for the rich. Fine mansions, Newport style though less opulent, lined Seagirt Boulevard. Few now remained; these were boarded up, weed-choked, crumbling reminders of a gracious and prosperous past.

It had been a fine place for a boy to grow up, Gary Reissig mused as he got into his car on this fine summer's day and headed down Beach Twentieth toward the shore. The channel hadn't been dredged for commercial boat traffic then, and you could swim across from the inland beaches to the ocean side; at low tide you could walk over. There was fishing and boating. In the winter, fresh-water ponds froze over for skating. It had been a family-oriented community.

As the railroad had brought the rich from the city, the subway had brought the underprivileged, and with them came slums. The Rockaways were now one of the most violent crime–infested sections of the five boroughs. Gangs not only still flourished, they raged rampant. Individuals, driven by inner devils to the breaking point, seemed here to go completely out of control. Downtown, merchants were frightened; business after business shut down. The streets appeared devastated. Youths, black and white, hung around the few shops and bars remaining, their idleness a threat. From the top of the hill before the road dipped, Reissig had a view of the shimmering waters of the Atlantic Ocean. There were a few sails and some beachgoers already out. The offshore breeze was brisk and cool. It might be sweltering in the city; out here it was at least fifteen degrees cooler. It would never be for his children the way it had been for him, Gary Reissig thought, but maybe the good that was left—both of moral values and of natural resource—might be preserved.

Across from the Wavecrest section, Reissig spotted two patrol cars alongside what undoubtedly had to be the victim's car. An old man in plaid shorts sat on the sand, his bicycle lying beside him. Reissig pulled over and got out. The first thing he looked at was the victim.

She was slumped partly against the steering wheel and partly against the driver's window. Curly auburn hair fell forward and hid her face, but not the welter of blood that made a broad collar around her neck. There was no need to feel for either of the carotid arteries. The knife had severed both.

Chapter

SIX

On Monday, the first day of the investigation into Nancy Hurlock's death, Norah had finished typing her preliminary report and was ready to go home by seven. Then she remembered Father Boylan. She had promised to drop by the rectory. Suddenly, she felt very tired. What could she really do to help Father? she asked herself. She should certainly talk to the detectives at the One-Seven. She consulted her notebook for their names: Ben Jones and Ed Gregory. They'd be gone by now. Norah was sure they would have already done everything possible; her visit to the priest would be merely a courtesy that could wait till tomorrow.

Nevertheless, Norah woke the next morning with the deferred obligation foremost in her mind. She rationalized that she had to finish the homicide report first, then check with Doc Worgan regarding the autopsy, and drive out to Great Neck to begin the interrogation of Nancy Hurlock's friends and neighbors. Father Boylan would understand the priorities. She would just get the latest on the theft of the chalice from the robbery squad and inform Father of any progress.

Jones and Gregory were out canvassing the pawnshops, she was told when she called from the office. Which was about all they could do and all, she told herself, she could have done. When she called the rectory, she learned Father

Boylan was out too. She left a message. She didn't attempt to analyze her relief in not having had to speak to him directly.

Among the messages for her were two from Adrian Gourdine. The DeVecchis were away in Vermont where they rented a house each summer, so for now the whole Toni situation was on hold. She tore up the art teacher's latest messages, as she had the earlier ones. Then she left, quickly. It was almost as though she were afraid that someone or something might detain her.

Most detectives considered canvassing a dreary part of an investigation. It afforded neither glamour nor excitement. Patience was the prime requisite. Most investigators were quickly bored. But Norah didn't discourage easily and she maintained her interest by dwelling on the personality of those she interviewed rather than letting herself get frustrated over a lack of results. She was surprised to discover as great a mix of background and attitude in suburbia as in the city.

Norah spoke to Nancy Hurlock's erstwhile schoolmates. She located them at the clubs and beaches. She enquired at the stores and restaurants and hangouts in the town. She interrogated everyone she could find who had had contact with the dead girl, but she learned nothing new—not about her habits or her character. Nancy remained the shy and introspective lonely girl she had appeared from the first. No one out here where she had lived had noticed as much change in her as had her boss at the bank; no one out here had cared enough. Norah understood. Her own childhood had been solitary. She too had had few friends and almost no dates. The difference was that Patrick Mulcahaney, Norah's father, had encouraged his daughter to get out, to have friends, had even tried to "fix her up," much to her embarrassment and annoyance. She smiled now thinking of the way Dad had introduced the young men one after another, having meticulously vetted each one first, of course. But

Jeffrey Hurlock had done everything he could to keep his daughter isolated.

The autopsy confirmed that the victim had not been sexually violated. So the body was released. Norah attended the funeral on Friday. Through the weekend she continued her interviews, catching those people who had been working during the week. Still, she didn't turn up anybody who had seen the dead girl in the company of anyone who might be described as a boyfriend. On Sunday, Norah decided that she had explored all reasonable possibilities. She intended to visit Mrs. Hurlock once more, but she wanted to go when Mr. Hurlock wasn't around; that meant waiting till Monday. So she grabbed some lunch in the backyard garden of a country restaurant and headed back. Passing over the Queensboro Bridge she could see the church of Our Lady of Perpetual Help to the right of the down ramp and felt the familiar twinge of guilt at having put off her visit with Father Boylan for so long. Today, Sunday, of course, was his busiest day. She would see him tomorrow. For sure.

"He wants you!" Art Potts called out to Norah as soon as she walked into the squad room.

She glanced at the captain's closed door. "What's up?"

Potts shrugged. "He's been asking for you at fifteen-minute intervals ever since lunch."

"Oh, boy." Norah grimaced, walked over, and knocked.

Manny Jacoby was forty-two years old, five eleven, paunchy, nearly bald. He looked more like your friendly neighborhood grocer than a police captain. Though in theory it shouldn't have mattered, his appearance hadn't helped him. Twice he'd taken and passed the captain's exam only to have the time limitation expire without appointment. On the third try he'd made the top of the list. Now he was as dogged in his determination to succeed as head of Homicide, Fourth Zone, as he had been in getting the job.

"You wanted me, Captain?"

"You didn't call in, Mulcahaney."

"There was nothing to report, Captain."

"You came up empty." It was merely a statement, but the tone indicated Manny Jacoby would have been surprised if she had turned up anything.

"Whoever the boyfriend was, he made sure not to be seen. I'm going to have one more talk with Mrs. Hurlock . . ."

"Why? It's not likely the mother would have held back information that could lead to her child's killer."

"She's afraid. I'm not sure why." Norah was reluctant to enlarge on what was only a hunch—the captain wasn't big on hunches—so she changed the subject. "Did the lab turn up anything in Nancy's car?"

He shook his head. "Maybe we won't need anything."

Norah waited. He would tell her in his own time. It was the reason he had been calling for her so incessantly.

"Doc Worgan was trying to reach you."

"He was?" That really surprised her.

"When you weren't available he talked to me."

Norah bit back a smile. The captain didn't like that. Manny Jacoby was a good cop with years of investigative experience. As an administrator, he was simply afraid to delegate. He constantly checked on everybody, trying to keep abreast of every detail of every investigation and juggling assignments so no one officer could have greater knowledge of any single case than he did himself. Choked with facts, his concentration diffused, he was becoming anxious and irritable. Also, in this heat his feet hurt worse than usual.

"According to Doc Worgan we may be dealing with a mass killer. The body of another young woman was found this morning out on the island. Actually, on this side of the city line. Sitting in her car. Her throat was cut."

Norah waited for more details.

"She was in her twenties."

"That's all? Nancy Hurlock wasn't in her car when she was killed."

"I know that, Mulcahaney. I read the reports, but the m.o. was the same. Each victim was young, single, and drove her own car. We don't want the media pointing that out before we do."

"No sir, but . . ."

"What?"

"We don't want them stressing the similarities. We don't want to frighten the public. Maybe we should admit the cases are somewhat alike, but play it down."

Jacoby was a fair man. He thought it over. "Okay. Sounds good to me. That's how we'll play it for now." He winced. The captain wore special shoes to support his fallen arches and accommodate his bunions; they didn't always help. "Too bad you didn't get a look at the scene while you were out there. If you'd taken the trouble to call in you could have spared yourself a trip."

"No problem, Captain. I'll go back . . ."

"Not now, Mulcahaney!" He barked as Norah started for the door. The captain wanted a high ratio of arrests and cases cleared, but he also wanted to stay within his budget, and having detectives work overtime was not the way to do it. "Tomorrow." The strain on his face eased. Under the desk, Jacoby had slipped off his shoes. "You go out there first thing tomorrow morning. See Detective Reissig."

At exactly eight A.M. the next morning Norah made the turn from Far Rockaway Boulevard onto Mott Avenue. Two blocks over was the start of the subway line from Far Rockaway to Manhattan. Passengers were congregating from all directions. In an area of cheap stores and bars, of abandoned buildings and refuse-strewn streets, men in well-pressed expensive business suits carried genuine leather briefcases and mingled with blue-collar workers, mounting the stairs, sweating, to the elevated platform. They came from the more affluent surrounding communities. Their station cars filled the parking lots and lined the streets while the loiterers already stood at their posts watching—surly, brooding, envious. Only in one other place had Norah seen the juxtaposition of two such disparate economic groups— Times Square. As there, the police presence here was heavy and alert.

Under the circumstances, Norah decided that leaving her little Honda in front of the station house in a no-parking zone would not get her off to a good start. She kept circling and finally settled for a spot four blocks away. By the time she walked back it was eight-twenty. She hoped she wasn't too late.

She needn't have worried. Gary Reissig was at his desk, feet up, enjoying the morning's coffee and pastry, apparently in no hurry to go anywhere.

"Detective Reissig? Good morning. I'm Norah Mulcahaney. Homicide, Manhattan."

"Sergeant Mulcahaney. Sure. They told me you'd be coming." He looked her over, frankly curious. Norah was wearing a beige linen dress she had left unbelted for coolness while driving; on arrival she'd tied it at the waist with an orange sash. Her dark hair was pulled back and tied with a matching ribbon. She wore white flat sandals. Her cheeks were slightly flushed from the hot walk, her dark blue eyes were bright, eager, and confident.

Reissig stuck out his hand but didn't get up. "Have a seat, Sergeant. Coffee? Piece of Danish?"

"Thanks. Both."

In turn she assessed him, routinely: blonde, stocky, tanned and fit. Middle or late thirties. Colorfully but neatly dressed in bright tomato slacks and a gray knit LaCoste shirt. He smiled. She smiled back and looked more searchingly. The tan was layers deep, composed of summer sun and winter wind. His stomach was hard and flat; the shoulders well-developed. That weathered look was rare among cops sentenced to year-round pallor, to desk slouch and beer bloat. Despite his easy manner, there was a well of reserve behind Reissig's gray eyes. Shyness? Hardly. Few cops with that quality survived. Resentment of her presence? There was no indication of it, no sign he was disturbed to have somebody from the city out to look over his shoulder. A nice change, Norah thought as he placed the coffee and cake before her.

She sipped and munched.

"What can I do for you, Sergeant?"

"We were advised by the medical examiner's office that there are certain similarities between a homicide you're carrying and one of ours that occurred just a week ago."

"Yeah, right. We have a female Caucasian, about twenty-three or -five. She was found yesterday morning sitting in her car, throat slashed. She bled to death."

Norah nodded. "We have a female Caucasian, twenty-two, who died in the same manner, though she wasn't inside her car. It was parked nearby."

"No sexual violation," Reissig told her. "As far as we know now."

"Not in our case either. That's definite according to the autopsy. She was fully clothed."

"Right. Have you turned up a motive?"

"We think she had a boyfriend she was seeing secretly. We think they may have had a fight. The evidence suggests she had a date with him, but we can't get proof. Nobody ever saw them together."

"Our man was going steady with the victim; everybody knew about it. He hung out at the diner where she worked as a waitress. Wanted to marry her, but she was putting him off. He couldn't take it. Had a big fight with her. Plenty of witnesses."

The circumstantial evidence and the m.o. were certainly alike, but the character of the boyfriend appeared to be very different. Norah was puzzled by Reissig's nonchalance. He'd done good work getting a background on the victim so quickly and even turning up a likely suspect. She would have expected him to be impatient to get back out on the trail. Instead, he was behaving as if there was no urgency. And he was not only being very cooperative with someone from another command, but seemingly enjoying himself doing it.

"I don't see our man carrying on with both women at the same time," Reissig commented in that same lazy fashion that puzzled Norah. "He doesn't seem the type. Of course, in our business you can never be sure." He grinned. "You could talk to him if you want."

Norah stared. "You've located him?"

He beamed. "Better than that. We've got him. Downstairs. In a holding cell."

"You've made the collar?"

"Right."

"In less than twenty-four hours?"

"We expect him to be arraigned this afternoon and go before the grand jury in Mineola on Wednesday."

"That's . . . impressive, Detective Reissig."

"Call me Gary."

"Has he confessed?"

"Come on, Sergeant, you can't have everything."

"No, no, I'm not criticizing. To the contrary. I didn't expect . . . It's remarkable work. Call me Norah."

"Well, Norah," Reissig tilted his head to one side in a deprecating manner. "It was open and shut. Baffler, that's the suspect, was crazy about the woman. She threw him over for another man. They quarreled . . . like I told you, in front of plenty of witnesses. She drove off and left him standing. He went to her house. She wasn't there. He waited. When she showed up, he got into her car and they had one more argument. Then he killed her."

"What about the other man?" Norah asked. "Maybe he did it."

Reissig shrugged. "Why should he? If there was another man."

Reissig must surely be aware of all other possibilities in the case, so for the time being Norah decided not to bring them up. "You really mean I can talk to him? What about his lawyer?"

"You don't have to worry; he wants to talk. He'll tell you about her, about himself, about her kid and his mother. He'll tell you more than you want to know."

Chapter

SEVEN

Howard Baffler was grieving. He had metamorphosed overnight. Baffler no longer stooped so much as sagged; he shuf-
fled rather than walked, the strength even to lift his feet
drained away. His ruddy coloring had faded to gray, the
freckles ugly blotches; his red hair muddied to brown. He
was shaken not by his own danger but by the death of May
Guttman. Observing him as he was led into the interrogation
room and physically steered into a chair, Norah knew he was
not aware of the gravity of his own situation.

Reissig introduced her. "This is Detective Sergeant
Mulcahaney from New York, Howard. She wants to ask you
some questions—mostly about another case. You don't
have to talk to her if you don't want to."

"I didn't kill May. As God is my witness, I didn't do it."

"You may have an attorney present at this interview if you
wish, Mr. Baffler," Norah was careful to advise him.

"I'm innocent."

"If you do decide to talk to me, what you tell me may be
used as evidence against you. Do you understand that, Mr.
Baffler?"

"I'm innocent. I didn't kill May. I have nothing to hide."
Reissig and Norah exchanged glances: how many times had
they both heard that protestation and how many times had

the willing cooperation of a self-assured suspect led to his own conviction?

Holding back a sigh, Norah pulled out a chair and sat down at the table across from the suspect. Reissig sat at the end.

"Now, Mr. Baffler, where were you a week ago Sunday night? Not last night, but Sunday the eleventh?"

"May died last night. No, Saturday night. She died Saturday night while I was waiting for her in front of her house. All night long I waited . . ."

"We'll talk about that later. For now, just tell me where you were a week ago yesterday: the eleventh of July."

It took him a while. "Home. I was home. I don't work Sundays anymore. May wasn't feeling well. She broke our date. So I was home having a few beers and watching the double-header on TV."

"What kind of work do you do, Mr. Baffler?"

"Trucker. I work for the Cosmopolitan Transportation Company."

"And what was the double-header you were watching?"

"Mets versus Cincinnati."

Sunday double-headers were rare. Norah happened to know about this one; the second game was a makeup game. She followed the Mets because Joe had. "Do you live alone, Mr. Baffler?"

"Yes, ma'am. My mom died six months ago."

"I'm sorry. Did you watch the game with anyone? Did anybody call on the telephone that evening? Did you step outside at any time and speak with a neighbor?" At each query he shook his head. "In other words, Mr. Baffler, there's no one who can support the fact that you were home that night as you claim?"

"Nobody called. I didn't talk to anybody. I was alone."

Norah sighed openly. She unzipped her purse and took out a photograph of Nancy Hurlock she had gotten from the girl's mother. "Do you know her?"

"No, ma'am."

"She looks something like May though, wouldn't you say? Except for the hair." Norah put her hands over the hair. "Look just at her face."

"She's not as pretty." Baffler's eyes filled.

Norah turned to Reissig, speaking low. "I'd like to ask him some questions about Saturday."

Reissig was smart enough and a good enough judge of people to know that Mulcahaney wasn't going to shake loose easily. Having invited her to start, he might as well let her finish or she'd turn out to be a bigger headache later. Besides, what could she ask that hadn't already been covered? Confident, he shrugged; she could suit herself.

Norah pulled up closer to the table and thus closer to the suspect. "All right, Mr. Baffler, tell me about Saturday night. You had a fight with May."

He frowned and looked down. "We had a date and she called it off. It was the fourth time in two weeks she'd stood me up." He appealed to Norah, brown eyes hurt. "What could I think? I mean, the message was plain, right? There had to be another man. I wanted to know and I didn't want to know, get what I mean? I was afraid to ask too much for fear of pushing her into breaking off for good. I figured as long as she didn't actually tell me who he was and how serious it was between them, well maybe it would blow over. I loved her. I was willing to wait it out. Then I thought that if I could find out who the man was without her knowing . . . I could warn him off." Baffler's ravaged face hardened. Out of his dulled eyes a gleam of light flashed. "I thought I'd kill him if I had to." Then it was gone. "I wish I had."

"You found out who it was?"

The prisoner shook his head. "He'd be dead by now instead of May. He should be."

"Let's get back to the argument in the diner, Mr. Baffler. May ran out the back through the employees' rest room and you chased after her."

"By the time I got there she was in her car and pulling out

of the parking lot. I couldn't catch her, not with my rig. I still had a delivery to make. So I did that. Then I checked out at the depot and picked up my own car. I drove to May's place. She wasn't there. I hadn't expected she would be." He sighed heavily. "I waited. I waited all night. She didn't come. I went home."

"What time did you leave?"

"I don't know. It was light."

"Did anybody see you leave?"

"I don't know."

Again Norah looked to Reissig, who shrugged. "Well, Mr. Baffler, did anybody see you when you got back to your own place?"

He'd stopped listening.

Slowly, Norah rose. With a nod she indicated to Reissig that she was through. He rang for a guard to escort the prisoner back to his cell. When Baffler had been taken away, the two detectives walked out together.

"So?" Reissig asked.

"Did anybody see May Guttman come home that night?"

"There's a bar and disco at the end of her block. It's open till four A.M. on weekends; by the time the regulars disperse, it's more like five A.M. People in the neighborhood sleep with their shades down and earplugs."

"So nobody saw her and Baffler together that night?"

"We've established motive and opportunity. We don't have eyeball witnesses."

"You only have opportunity if you assume that Guttman came back while Baffler was still waiting for her."

"Okay." Reissig agreed to the obvious.

"Where did she live?"

"West Long Beach."

"And she was killed in her car parked in Far Rockaway. So you also have to ask me to believe that she not only got home and met Baffler, but that he left his car, got into hers, and they drove to the scene together."

"Okay."

"Why?" Norah insisted. "Why should he do that? Why didn't he talk to her right there where he was?"

"Maybe he figured a stroll along the water would be romantic and help his cause. How do I know?"

"But she lived right near the beach, didn't she? Why drive across the bridge? Why go in her car? He'd have had to leave his own car behind and then come back for it after he killed her. That's a long walk. Unless they went in separate cars, and that makes no sense at all."

"What are you trying to do, Norah? Mess up my case?"

Norah took a deep breath, raised her chin, and looked straight at Reissig. "I'm sorry, but Howard Baffler isn't the man we want."

"I'm sorry that you made the trip for nothing."

"I mean you've got the wrong man. He didn't kill May Guttman."

Reissig's tanned face darkened. His gray eyes were angry. "I've been fair with you, Norah. I've gone out of my way to accommodate—"

"Have you got an estimated time of death yet? Have you been able to verify when Baffler got back to his own place? Is it possible May was still alive when he returned home?"

"Who the hell do you think you're dealing with? I've been in this business as long as you have, lady—at least. It's too early for an autopsy report."

"That's my point."

"I don't know whether you're accusing me of stupidity or of trying to railroad an innocent man. Either way, I resent it."

"I didn't intend either, honestly. I apologize."

"Did you ever hear of professional courtesy?"

"Why do you refuse to even consider the possibility that somebody else did it?"

"Who? The other man? There is no other man except in Baffler's jealous imagination."

"How can you be sure?"

"May Guttman was pretty and popular. She dated a lot and she made no secret that she played around. Everybody at the diner, employees and customers, knew it. They also heard her tell Howie that there was no other special man."

Reissig steered Norah down the corridor toward the front door.

"Obviously, he didn't believe her. You talked to him yourself, you could see that he didn't believe her. Look, Howie Baffler was a Mama's boy. You want to know if I talked to his neighbors? I sure as hell did. And they all say he's a great guy, likes to drink with the other guys at the local saloon and did his share of chasing. But he never got serious before. In fact, all a girl had to do was hint at marriage and he dropped her, fast. Because of Mama. At age twenty-eight, Howie tried to be a man. Out of his own mouth, he was crazy about May Guttman. I've got witnesses that say he bugged her. I've got witnesses to say this was not the first time Baffler sat in front of her house waiting to see whether or not she came home alone. And they had arguments—loud, for everybody to hear, in which he threatened to kill himself if she wouldn't have him. Maybe she didn't want to be a substitute mother. Anyway, he couldn't take the rejection. He cracked up and instead of killing himself, he killed her."

They were at the exit.

"I don't think that May Guttman had any other really serious boyfriends. I think she just got fed up with Howie and told him so." Reissig held the door for Norah.

"I'm confident that the grand jury will bring in an indictment."

Gary Reissig had been sincere, but he hadn't answered Norah's questions. Why had the murder been committed in the victim's car? Why had it taken place so far from either her home or his? Norah couldn't attempt an explanation until she had more background on the crime. She went to the nearest pay telephone.

"They've made an arrest, Captain," she told Manny Jacoby.

"Already?"

She could visualize the scowl on his pudgy face melting into dismay, then annoyance that another command had gotten such fast results.

"Any possibility he could be the man we want too?"

"No, sir. Howard Baffler, that's the suspect, didn't commit either crime. They've got the wrong man."

"Is that so?" Jacoby was silent for a few moments. "You've told them that, I suppose?"

"I had to."

"Sure." He took a deep breath. "Okay, come on in, Mulcahaney."

"Sir, I thought I'd stop by and talk to Mrs. Hurlock. As long as I'm out here more or less in the vicinity . . ."

"Sure, sure, you might as well. Meantime I'll get in touch with whoever's in command out there and explain . . . You do have an explanation, a reason for thinking they've collared the wrong man . . ."

"Could you hold off, Captain?" Norah broke in, usually not a wise thing to do.

"What for?" Jacoby demanded.

"I think they'll postpone arraignment and review the evidence. It's just a hunch, of course."

Norah found the note taped to the Hurlocks' front door: *Can't hear the bell. I'm in the back. Come around. Thank you.*

Following instructions, she walked down the driveway and around the garage to a tree-shaded backyard. Mrs. Roseanne Hurlock was on her knees weeding around a bed of floribunda roses. Sensing a presence, she looked up and over her shoulder. When she saw Norah, the casual greeting was choked off.

"I'm sorry. I didn't mean to startle you." Norah smiled.

"I was expecting the plumber. Mrs. Hurlock's frosted hair was covered by a dark blue bandana. Her well-made-up face was streaked with dirt and tears. She looked at Norah through a mist.

"What a beautiful garden you have. Your roses are magnificent."

"It was Nancy's garden. She landscaped our whole plot and looked after it. The roses were her special joy."

"Gardening is a marvelous hobby."

"Not for a young girl. It's too solitary." Mrs. Hurlock bowed her head as tears welled up afresh.

Norah had to disregard her sorrow. "Nancy was twenty-two, yet she'd never had a serious boyfriend? Is that right?"

The mother nodded without looking up.

"Till recently," Norah continued. "She did meet somebody recently. She started going with him and she cared about him deeply. Isn't that so?"

Mrs. Hurlock didn't answer by word or look.

Norah got down and sat on the grass beside Nancy Hurlock's mother and waited for a few moments. She smelled the freshly cut lawn, the turned earth; she was warmed by the sun on her back. The bereaved woman was not even aware of these pleasures, could get no solace from them. "Mrs. Hurlock, I came particularly so we could talk without your husband overhearing. I think that Mr. Hurlock was very strict with Nancy, and very protective of her."

Mrs. Hurlock looked up, grateful for the understanding. "Yes, that's true. He meant for the best."

"Of course he did. But he did discourage the young men that Nancy brought home."

"Nobody was ever good enough." The mother sighed. "He put them through an embarrassing interview, both for the boy and for Nancy. If a young man survived it, Jeffrey ridiculed him to her afterwards. He spoiled it for her; so even if one of them cared enough to want to see her again, she was no longer interested."

How different her own father had been, Norah thought.

"He was so afraid Nancy would get in with the wrong

crowd, he couldn't see he was ruining her life, stunting her emotional growth."

"So when Nancy finally did find someone she cared about, she couldn't risk bringing him home," Norah concluded.

Mrs. Hurlock nodded and wearily passed a hand over her eyes.

"I understand that you didn't want to speak of it in front of your husband, Mrs. Hurlock, but this man Nancy was dating is the only lead we have. At the very least he could tell us what Nancy was doing on Sunday night. We have to find him."

No response.

"Nancy did tell you about him, didn't she? She did confide in you?"

At last the mother looked up and met Norah's eyes. "Yes."

Thank God, Norah thought. It was the first confirmation that the man she believed to be Nancy's murderer actually existed—not a stranger, not a psycho relieving his manic distress on a chance victim, but someone Nancy had known, trusted—loved.

"Did you ever meet him?" she asked.

"Oh, no."

"But Nancy talked about him, described him, maybe showed you a photo?"

"No photograph, but she did say he was very handsome, tall, dark, and young."

Norah was disappointed. "Where does he work?"

Mrs. Hurlock sank back on her heels away from the roses. The strain on her face and the tenseness of her body eased. "She didn't say. She just talked about how nice he was to her, how considerate."

"How did they meet?"

Having started, Mrs. Hurlock was now eager to talk, to tell what she knew. "Nancy was having lunch in a coffee shop near the bank—her regular place. He was at the counter beside her and accidentally spilled coffee on her jacket.

He wanted to pay for the cleaning but Nancy wouldn't let him. The next day he was waiting at the counter for her with a bunch of carnations.".

So, no mutual friend with whom to check back, Norah noted. She could visit the coffee shop and maybe she'd get lucky and somebody would remember the incident, but probably not. "They dated frequently?" she asked.

"Oh, I think she saw him every day."

"Over how long a period?"

"A couple of months. She told her father she had to work late on a special project."

"And you? What did she tell you."

The mother's face softened. "That she was in love."

She sighed and Norah sighed with her. Then Mrs. Hurlock returned to the present.

"You think he killed her, don't you?"

"We would like to talk to him. Did she tell you his name? His first name? Did she tell you where they went together? What restaurants, what bars? How did they spend their time?"

At each query Roseanne Hurlock shook her head. "Oh, God, my God! I should have asked. I should have made her tell me. Jeffrey was right to be strict. He was right. I was afraid to pry. I was afraid if I asked too many questions, she wouldn't come to me anymore. I wanted her to feel that I was on her side. I wanted her to feel that from me, at least, she had sympathy and support. I thought if I didn't support her, she might move out and get a place of her own like all the girls are doing. As long as she wasn't working for her father anymore, she could do as she pleased. Before, if she even talked about getting her own place, he would threaten to fire her. Working at the bank made her truly independent. I didn't want to lose her." She licked her lips as new tears threatened. "I didn't want to lose my child . . ."

The irony overwhelmed her. She cried and sobbed in great, gulping gasps. Gradually, she quieted and her countenance cleared. For a brief moment, she seemed almost content.

"I was glad for her. I thought that at twenty-two she should have, she was entitled to . . . the experience. I thought she should know love, even if it didn't result in marriage." Then all the regret and pain returned, more torturously than before. "I was wrong!" she cried out. "It's my fault. I should have told Jeffrey. He would have put a stop to it and Nancy would still be alive. God forgive me. Jeffrey never will."

Norah's hunch about Gary Reissig was right. He hadn't ignored her questions; he simply had not had the answers. As soon as she left the Mott Avenue station, he went out to get them. His first stop was West Long Beach and the house in which May Guttman had lived.

She had rented the upstairs apartment in a two-family house half a block from the ocean. The houses were detached but so close together there was only a footpath between. Everything was cement, both front and back yards. There were no lawns or gardens, only the odd rootbound shrub expiring in a pot beside a front door. The sun was brilliant though, and the breeze off the water fresh and exhilarating. A wall at the end of the street closed off access to the beach. There was a gate and the placard on it proclaimed: *Private Beach. Gate closed at eight P.M. Trespassers will be prosecuted.* The wall was waist high, but anybody could scale it by throwing a leg over the top. Mulcahaney's point was well taken, Reissig thought. If all May and Howie had wanted was to walk and talk a little, this stretch of beach was accessible and would have done as well as any other. If he had intended to kill her . . . maybe this stretch wasn't deserted enough. It didn't explain May's agreeing to take a drive with him after returning from another, presumably very late date. It didn't explain his going in her car. Reissig scowled. Damn Mulcahaney.

The broken spring under the seat pinched him as he got

out of the battered old station wagon. With two kids needing constant medical attention there wasn't money for a new car. Fixing it up didn't make sense when the youngsters were constantly stamping their feet on the upholstery and dribbling ice cream. Reissig sighed. Raising two handicapped children single-handed—the boy retarded, the girl deaf— wasn't easy. Sometimes it was heartbreaking and sometimes exasperating, but they were worth the cost, financial and emotional. Reissig smiled to himself and slammed the car door without bothering to lock it; who would bother to steal the old wreck? He looked around with the cop's habitually observing eye.

Though it was the middle of a bright day on which most people would be at the beach, there were a few old folk sitting dazedly in the shade of a front porch, a few women visible through kitchen windows getting the noon meal ready. The neighborhood was a mixture of retired people living on social security and meager pensions and college kids on vacation who worked at the various beach clubs during the day and partied all night. There was an uneasy truce between them. Reissig stopped in front of number thirty-two and looked up to the second-floor porch entrance of the apartment that had been May's. There was an outside staircase, but he didn't go up. He rang the bell below. He rang several times and was just about to walk away when a dark heavyset man with a beard appeared at the screen door. He yawned prodigiously.

"What do you want?" His eyes were bleary, the lids puffed and red.

"Mr. Harrington?" Reissig held up his ID. "Sorry to disturb you."

"It's okay. I got to be back to work in a couple of hours anyway. Just got off a sixteen-hour shift. What the hell!" He shrugged and yawned again, displaying flashes of gold crowns. "Lucky to have a job, I guess. What can I do for you . . . uh, Detective Reissig?"

Reissig knew that Harrington was an airline freight man-

ager for Eastern. A lot of airline personnel lived out here—
it was handy to both Kennedy and La Guardia—and their
schedules were as erratic as a cop's, almost. "I need to ask
you a few questions."

Harrington jerked his great head up toward the second
floor. "About May? I thought you got the guy that did it."

"We have a suspect." An hour ago he wouldn't have been
so circumspect, Reissig mused; an hour ago he had had no
idea that he would be back here. "When we were here before neither you nor your wife were at home."

"Right. The neighbors told us the police came. Joyce
works days and I work nights so when we manage to get a
day off at the same time, we try to make the most of it."

"Sure. Is it okay if I come in?"

"Oh, sorry, you bet." Charlie Harrington unlatched the
screen door and led the way into a small shabby living room
sparsely and cheaply furnished—a typical summer rental,
except that the Harringtons owned the house. It was a lot
cleaner than the usual rental, at least. It appeared that the
Harringtons took care of what they had.

"Coffee?"

"No thanks."

"Mind if I get some? I can't function till I've had my coffee
fix." Without waiting for a reply, Harrington moved across
the tiny room, furniture trembling at every step. He returned promptly, settled himself on the imitation leather
settee and lit a cigarette. From the way he inhaled, it was the
first of the day and the only one that really tasted good,
Reissig, who had recently given up smoking, observed his
pleasure wistfully.

"Okay, shoot."

"How long had May Guttman been your tenant?"

"A little over two years. She came in the winter—well,
right after Thanksgiving. We had just bought the house in
August and, you know, in the summer with the sun shining
everything looks good. Then it started to rain and we had
leaks; it got cold and the boiler broke down—what can I tell

you? We needed income and we hadn't really expected to get a tenant till summer so we were real glad to have her. On the other hand, we had to charge less being she was going to rent year round. And we weren't crazy about a woman alone with a little kid. We decided to give it a try."

"She had the child with her?"

"Oh, sure. Bobbie. Four years old when they came. He was a good kid, quiet, lonely. I used to play ball with him. I felt sorry for him. She had to get work where they'd let her bring Bobbie, then at night she had to stay home and watch him—she couldn't afford babysitters. A couple of times Joyce sat for her, but what the hell, she couldn't do it every night, right?"

Reissig nodded.

"Anyhow, it went like that through the winter. Then we found out she was putting Bobbie to bed and slipping out and leaving him alone. A couple of nights the kid woke up scared and crying. Joyce went up to comfort him and sat till May showed up, sometimes not till four or five A.M. So that couldn't go on."

Charlie Harrington's massive chest heaved. "We didn't want to throw them out, but there was another problem. Joyce and I don't have kids. We wanted to; we tried, but no luck. And we were starting to get real attached to Bobbie; know what I mean? May wasn't going to live upstairs forever. Sooner or later, she was going to move and Bobbie would go with her, so we told her she'd better go before it hurt us and him too much. It ended with her shipping the boy to her folks in Miami."

"When was that?"

"Just about a year ago. I remember it. Joyce was real upset." He sighed; plainly he had been too. "After that, everything changed. May got the waitressing job and made good tips and started to enjoy herself. She was out seven nights a week. I swear I don't know how she took the pace. And the turnover in guys was . . . terrific. But she didn't parade them, if you know what I mean. And nobody stayed the night. She was discreet, considerate of Joyce and me and the neighbors."

"Did she have one particular friend?"

"The guy you arrested—Baffler."

"You're sure?"

"He was her only steady," Harrington shrugged. "Come to think of it, there was an odd thing. A couple of weeks ago I heard somebody coming down the stairs from her place around three A.M. Right after, I heard her footsteps. That was unusual enough for me to get up and look out the window. May and a guy I didn't know were getting into her car. I wondered where they were could be going—it was a weeknight and everything around here shuts down by one A.M.

"What did this guy look like?"

"Jeez, I was half asleep and it was dark."

"Try to remember. Was he tall?"

"He was bent over getting into the car."

"Build? What kind of build—heavy, slight, medium?"

"Medium."

"Coloring? That's a good bright street light out there."

"They weren't under it. Okay, okay." Harrington drew his heavy eyebrows together in concentration. "He had dark, wavy hair. Brown or black. No, it had to be black because he was wearing a black shirt and his hair was the same."

"Did you see him more than once?"

"Now that you mention it, I did. Three times."

"And that's as much as you can tell me about him?"

"Look, after the first time I didn't pay any attention. Why should I? He was just another of May's boyfriends."

"Would you know him if you saw him again?"

"Oh, hell, Detective Reissig. I could maybe say: yeah, that looks like him, something like him. That's the best I could do. Okay? I was curious but not interested. Know what I mean?"

"Sure." Reissig didn't want to press the witness, certainly not antagonize him, but Harrington had seen a possible second suspect. "You said that the first time you observed the two of them they were getting into her car. Was she driving?"

"Right."

"The other times?"

"Now that you mention it, they always used her car."

"Did he ever drive?"

"Jeez, I don't know."

"Never mind. Don't worry about it. Let's talk about the night of the murder."

"Oh, now, hey! I don't know anything about that. I worked that night."

"How about your wife?"

"Joyce went to bed right after I left."

"So neither of you saw May at all that night?"

"We saw her when she first came home, a little after six. We thought she was supposed to be working late. Anyway, she went right out again just before seven. We didn't see her after that."

"She went alone in her car?"

"Right."

"What time did you leave for work?"

"Eleven-thirty."

"So you must have seen Howard Baffler waiting in his car."

"Sitting in it across the street, right. I didn't like the idea of May maybe coming back with the other guy and the two of them meeting, but what could I do? I mean, it wasn't my business, was it?"

That was an appeal often made and to which no answer was expected nor wanted. "So you have no idea what time May came back or whether she was alone?"

He shook his head.

"Or when Baffler left?"

"All I know is that there wasn't a row. Not here. If there had been, Joyce would have heard."

He was absolving them both, Reissig thought, and that

too was normal. "Okay, Mr. Harrington, thanks." He got up. "I appreciate the cooperation."

"I wish I could have been more helpful." The big man grunted himself to his feet.

"There is one more thing."

"Shoot."

"I'd like to send the fingerprint experts over to dust the apartment upstairs. Would that be all right?" It was always good PR to ask permission.

Harrington came fully awake. This was the real thing! "You bet."

"It hasn't been cleaned yet, I hope?"

"No, no. Joyce called May's folks and they said pack everything and send it on. She hasn't had a chance to do it yet."

"Good. Ask her to leave everything like it is for a couple of days, will you? I'd appreciate it. And if you could let me have that Miami phone number?"

Once out on the street, Gary Reissig didn't head for his car but for the dead end, where he sat on the low wall looking out across the sand to the sea. He had learned two things from Charlie Harrington: first, there definitely had been another man besides Baffler in May Guttman's life; second, he didn't have a car of his own.

Chapter

EIGHT

Norah nearly went by the turnoff. She usually took the Long Island Expressway to Queens Boulevard and then the Queensboro Bridge to get back in to the city. On this hot July afternoon she was tempted to keep on to the Grand Central, taking her across the Triboro instead, and then down the East River Drive to Seventy-ninth. She reasoned that, as she wasn't going home but back to the precinct it would actually be quicker, but she knew the real reason was that the usual way would bring her too close to Our Lady of Perpetual Help. In fact, if she took the still under renovation upper roadway, the down ramp would put her right in front of the church and rectory, the scene of Sister Therese's murder.

Solving the elderly nun's death had been high priority for Norah and her task force, but she and the group of expert detectives had failed on the murder. Everything pointed to a random wanton attack by a stranger on a stranger. Sister Therese had been stabbed to death on the steps between the upper and lower churches in the shadow of the bridge. While Norah investigated the murder, her husband, Joe Capretto, was shot down in a parking lot under another bridge. In Norah's mind, and in her emotions, the two crimes intertwined.

The call reporting Sister Therese's murder had come to

Norah just at the end of her tour. She could have passed it on; she should have; but she had elected to catch it herself. So she called Joe at his office at headquarters to tell him she'd be late getting home. Since she was working late, Joe had decided to do the same. As executive officer for the chief of detectives, Captain Capretto always had plenty of work to catch up on. He had stayed till nearly eight that night. Otherwise he wouldn't have walked into a nearly empty parking lot. He wouldn't have interrupted an attempted rape, been shot and run down, caught in the undercarriage of the getaway car and dragged through the streets of Chinatown. Norah had only to see the scene of the nun's death to mentally recreate the other. And the other was more vivid.

But she had promised Father Boylan to stop by and she couldn't in conscience put it off any longer. Clenching her teeth, Norah veered left to the Queens Boulevard exit. Thirty minutes later she came off the bridge and was parking on the all-too-familiar block.

It hadn't changed since that bleak winter evening. As then, it was deserted. The fenced-in recycling section under the ramp was closed—she couldn't remember ever having seen it open. The alley from Sixtieth to Sixty-first was littered with dog droppings stinking in the heat. The brilliant sky above emphasized the squalor below. The yellow brick church, long since faded to dingy gray, and the rectory with its red-brick Victorian façade were plainly impoverished and forgotten, out of their time and place. It was the school on the adjoining block that kept the convent and the whole complex going. Two years ago it was a coed grammar and junior high school. The nuns hadn't been able to handle the violence; now it was an all-girl high school devoted to teaching technical skills. Norah wondered how long it could last in that guise.

She climbed the steps to the rectory, rang the bell, and was buzzed in.

"Sergeant Mulcahaney!" The lay worker at the switchboard beamed. "It's good to see you."

"Thanks. How are you, Shirley?"

"Surviving," she replied cheerfully. Shirley Arkin was forty and overweight and destined to remain a spinster. Though she accepted her lot, she went on fantasizing. "We had a robbery last week in the church. He just walked in and helped himself."

"I heard." Norah nodded. Her skin felt clammy; her stomach in knots. To her left was the parlor where Jim Felix had told her Joe had been shot. Carefully, she kept her back to it; nevertheless she could still see the yellowed, much-mended lace curtains through which she'd watched for the inspector's arrival not knowing the news he would bring but sensing the impending disaster. Each time she came here she hoped the memories would be less acute, but they didn't soften.

"What can we do for you, Sergeant?"

Norah forced herself back to the present and returned Shirley Arkin's smile. "I came to see Father Boylan."

"Gosh, I think you just missed him. He said he was going jogging. Wait a sec'." Shirley plugged into the board and listened while an extension somewhere at the back of the rectory rang. She started to shake her head at Norah, then grinned instead. "Father? Sergeant Mulcahaney's here to see you . . . I will, Father." She disconnected. "Go through, Sergeant, to Parlor A." She pressed the button releasing the inside door.

Father Albert Boylan, pastor of Our Lady of Perpetual Help parish, including the National Shrine of the Blessed Infant of Praque, was tall and gaunt. He had sharp features dominated by a hawk nose. At the same time, his brow was clear and his brown eyes mild. He was young for the post and in sweat shirt and running shorts, spindly legs and bony knees exposed, he looked even younger and certainly not like a priest. In fact, with the light from the window behind him silhouetting his gangly frame and casting an aura around his curly head while throwing his face into shadow, he could have passed for a teenager. Norah felt a pang for an innocence Father Boylan had retained despite his contact with the ills and evils of the world. She had lost it.

The pastor flushed. "Forgive my appearance, please."

"I've come at a bad time," she apologized.

"Never, Norah. I know, strictly speaking, this is not in your jurisdiction, but I thought you'd want to know about it. The detectives who came were very sympathetic but I don't believe they understood the import of what I told them."

"How's that, Father?"

"You see, what was stolen—the chalice—was our only valuable piece. The sole treasure, speaking in terms of cash, our church possessed. I think I told you that."

"Yes, Father."

"Our church is poor. That's all too obvious. It certainly isn't the kind of place that offers temptation to the casual thief—not like St. Pat's, for instance."

"No, Father."

"So whoever took the chalice had seen it before and had some idea of its monetary value."

"A parishioner?"

"I don't like to think that. I don't think that. Our people are mostly old and all poor. You've seen them, Norah. It may be little, but they all give to the church. They don't take."

Norah remained silent, waiting.

"The chalice disappeared sometime between the end of the seven A.M. mass and the start of the eight on Monday morning. It's not likely that a casual thief would drop in for daily mass."

"You think it's one of the pupils at the school?" Norah was more saddened than surprised.

Father Boylan sat down at the little parlor table. "We have two hundred girls. I know them individually. I would say no."

"Then I don't follow."

"I want the chalice back, Norah, of course I do, but that's not why I asked you to come. 'Vengeance is mine; I will repay, saith the Lord,' Romans 12:19. I know that He works in His own way and in His own time, but there's nothing that says we can't lend a helping hand."

Norah bit back a smile: Father Boylan was a true Christian pragmatist.

"The last time, the only time, we had a robbery here was when Sister Therese was killed."

The poor box had been pried open with a knife. The thief had come running out of the church with the contents, possibly ten dollars in coins, and been surprised by the nun. "You think it could be the same person."

"I do."

"Did you mention this to Jones and Gregory?"

"They weren't impressed."

"It's long odds, Father. We tried to trace the killer back then. If you recall, we not only checked all of Sister's pupils in the neighborhood, but most of those who had moved, on the theory that one might have returned."

"But you had nothing to go on then. Now you do. You have the chalice. He'll sell it or pawn it, won't he?"

He looked so eager, so hopeful. "Sell it probably, Father, to a fence. I'm sure the detectives canvassed the pawnshops. If they'd turned up anything, they would have notified you. I'm afraid it's too late."

"I don't believe it." The pastor's eyes were bright. "They couldn't have covered every pawnshop in the city."

That was certainly true, Norah thought. "I don't know any pawnshop that would take it, but let's say he found one—I doubt the piece would appear on the list of acquisitions all pawnshops are required to submit to the police."

"Give it a try, Norah, please."

Norah hesitated, she hated to tell him, but she had to. "Father, a religious article like that, with a history, easily traceable, couldn't be disposed of intact. To get rid of it, the fence would pry out the stones and then melt down the gold and sell it by weight."

Father Boylan's face remained cheery. "They told me."

"It's just as close to hopeless as anything can be, Father."

"The Lord did not let our chalice be taken without a reason."

Norah sighed.

"I know that coming here isn't easy for you." The pastor fixed his gentle brown eyes on her. "I know the associations are painful. I pray to the Lord that He will ease them."

And he had done what he could by sparing her the interview in the main parlor, she thought. "Covering the pawnshops in this town is not a one-man job, Father." She made a last attempt to get out of it. "I've got a heavy work load right now. I don't know when I could find the time," she protested.

But she had, in fact, already capitulated—and they both knew it.

The messages on Norah's desk were routine except for the copy of the autopsy report on Nancy Hurlock she had requested. She noted nothing new; it confirmed the manner of her death and detailed the number and precise location of the wounds. Time of death was estimated at nine hours after her last meal. Since the picnic had been untouched, Norah would have to check with the Hurlocks to find out when Nancy had last eaten—if that had been at home. Most important, the autopsy revealed that the victim had not been sexually abused. Nancy Hurlock had been a virgin.

The phone rang.

"Homicide, Sergeant Mulcahaney." Noting that it was well after four, Norah looked around for Roy Brennan, who was supposed to take over.

"Well, Sergeant, at last. This is Adrian Gourdine."

For a moment, Norah didn't place him.

He sensed it and he didn't like it. "Don't you remember me? I've been calling and calling."

"I remember you, Mr. Gourdine, and I've received your messages. I haven't had a chance to get back to you. I'm surprised you called me here."

"You're never home either. You're a busy lady." He was trying to play it light.

Norah didn't go along. "How did you find out I'm a police officer?"

"Antonia told me."

"She's out of town with her family."

"I asked her all about you the night of the reception. I was very interested."

"I see. Well, what can I do for you, Mr. Gourdine?"

"I'd like to talk to you."

"We are talking."

"I mean in person. Look, Sergeant Mulcahaney, I think we got off on the wrong foot."

"Do you?"

"I understand you're very attached to Antonia. You don't have children so you think of her as your own daughter."

Norah was instantly defensive. "I think of her as my niece."

Gourdine sensed he'd taken the wrong approach. "I'm sorry, I don't mean to intrude. Please, give me a chance to start over. Meet me. Have dinner with me. Afterwards, if you still feel Antonia shouldn't take my course this winter, well, that'll be it. I'll tell her she's not ready, that she should wait another year. Fair enough?"

"There's no need for a meeting, Mr. Gourdine."

"All right." He sighed. "Okay. You're right. The truth is that I want to see you again. The child is an excuse."

This time Norah was left without a quick answer.

"So when can I pick you up? Seven?"

"Tonight?"

"Why not? Unless you have something else on."

She hesitated. Why pretend? "Make it seven- thirty," she replied and smiled. She was about to hang up. "Oh. You don't know where I live."

"Yes, I do."

He hung up.

Norah dressed carefully. It wasn't a date; she didn't go out on dates. She couldn't even think of another man, not yet—maybe never. Her social life consisted mainly of family gatherings. The family was Joe's, and as it was large someone was always having a birthday or anniversary, a christening or graduation. Occasionally, she was invited to dinner at the home of another cop where she was either the only guest or the odd woman. Sometimes on the way home she stopped at the local hangout for a beer with the other off-duty cops. And that was it. Nobody tried to "fix her up" the way her father had and she was grateful.

She should have told Gourdine to see her at the precinct. That would have been the place for their discussion, Norah thought as she surveyed herself in the mirror on the back of her bedroom door. The dress she had chosen was a very dark blue silk. She wore a long necklace of turquoise stones Joe had given her on their third anniversary. Too fancy, she decided. It gave the . . . meeting . . . too much importance. She glanced at her watch—only seven, plenty of time to change. Slacks would be casual. Her black silk pants and black-and-white overblouse would be elegant but understated. Still, she was ready much too early. She should have agreed to seven o'clock, Norah thought. She shouldn't have agreed to see him at all. Why did he want to take her out anyway? He claimed to be attracted to her, but she certainly hadn't given him any encouragement. Standing at her window, Norah spotted Gourdine striding up the block.

She turned away. It would have been better to postpone any meeting till she'd had a chance to look into his background, to know something more about him than that he was an art teacher who took private pupils on the side. The doorbell rang and she went to let him in.

She had to admit that in spite of all the facial hair, which she personally didn't like, he was very good-looking. He was tall and fit, stomach hard and flat. His features were neatly chiseled and his eyes, though small, intrigued her by their unusual amber shade. He was dressed in dark slacks and a madras jacket. For a moment he paused on the threshold looking her over with appreciation. Then he made a slight, ceremonious bow and presented her with an old-fashioned nosegay, complete to the single red rose in the center and white paper frill collar.

"Truce?"

Norah had to smile. "Thank you." She took the bouquet and inhaled its sweet scent. "I didn't think they made these up anymore."

"I thought you'd like it."

Did she detect a mocking note? Even as she chided herself for being overly suspicious, he had walked past her and was looking around.

"Nice place."

"Thank you. Would you like a glass of white wine?"

"Fine." He didn't offer to help but sat down, seeming very much at ease. When Norah returned from the kitchen and handed him a glass he raised it and looked into her eyes. "Here's to better understanding."

They drank.

"So. First order of business: what do I call you? Sergeant is, well, intimidating. Mrs. Capretto? Much too formal."

"How about Norah?"

"I didn't dare."

This time there was no doubt of his intent and Norah laughed.

"Good. Next: where would you like to eat?"

"You name it."

"My place."

At her alarm, he laughed. "Can't blame a guy for trying. Seriously, I have a loft downtown in the Tribeca. I have my studio there too and it's where I hold my classes. It's absolutely nonthreatening and I would like you to see it—sometime, "he added grinning. "I think I should also tell you I'm not keen about teaching, either in the public school system or privately. I do it because I have to. I have no vocation for it. I need the money. I have my own work. I'm an artist. Unfortunately, the public doesn't know about me because the agents and the critics are too obtuse to understand, much less appreciate, what I do." The smile accompanying this pronouncement was tight, and calculated to underscore his bitterness.

"I consider teaching a dreary job, a dead end. I don't go for that bit about stimulating young minds." He paused for a moment. "Baloney!" Quite obviously he had something stronger in mind. "My father was a teacher and it's one of the things he used to say when the paycheck wouldn't stretch far enough. In spite of that, or maybe because of it, I am a good teacher. I don't encourage the untalented, and those I consider to have promise I don't delude about their limitations or the returns they can expect in the marketplace. Who knows better than me—on both scores?

"As for your Antonia—Toni—she does have a talent, but it's limited. She can develop into the kind of artist who sells through decorators because the painting suits the client's color scheme. I'm not knocking it; just because it's commercial doesn't mean it's not valid. After all, the great artists produced their best works on commission. It could be a good career if she'll be satisfied at that level. Or she can marry and paint as a sideline. Or as a hobby. I do need pupils, but I'm not so desperate I have to seduce a fifteen-year-old girl for the tuition."

Over all, it had been a pleasant evening. She had actually enjoyed herself, Norah realized after Adrian Gourdine brought her home. He had been attentive. She discounted that; it was his inbred style. The charm was automatic, turned on for any woman. In the restaurant, a small French bistro type only three blocks away, which she had never even noticed before, they hadn't talked about Toni at all. What had they talked about? General things and, surprisingly in view of the afterglow she felt, they hadn't agreed on much. It had been the exchanges, the thrust and parry, the way that he forced her to think, to use her mental agility as she seldom did anymore except in her work, that had been stimulating.

At her door he had asked to come in for a nightcap. Routine. She begged off because of an early morning call. All standard. He didn't argue. But he did make a final statement on Toni.

"As for an honest, emotional involvement with her, I go for mature women, perferably with high intelligence." His eyes bore into Norah's.

He was telling her he was attracted to her. Along with the disarming honesty, it was all technique. He almost couldn't help it, Norah thought. Though she knew it, she found herself responding and she was annoyed.

"And don't worry about my losing a pupil," he assured her. "I can only take so many and if you decide that being my pupil would be harmful to Toni, there are others eagerly waiting to fill her slot." The right corner of his mouth went up in a tilted smile and the right eyebrow rose with it.

"You might even consider taking up painting. You could use a hobby."

The remark stayed with Norah as he intended it should. She alternated between indignation and amusement. If Toni were to continue with her art studies, Norah decided, another teacher could be found. If her interest was truly in art and not in Adrian, she would accept that. Either way, she— Norah—couldn't see him again. He had made it impossible.

Norah put him out of her mind. She was good at that, usually. This time it took a phone call from Gary Reissig three days later to complete the job.

Chapter NINE

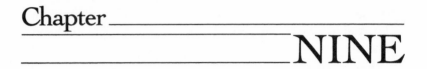

Mitch Ferris drew his racket back, set up, and hit through the ball—a sweeping, deep backhand that nicked the corner of the side and base lines of his opponent's left court. A lunge, followed by a desperate out of control swing, and the ball went sailing into the empty stands. *Out!*

There was no linesman to call it. No umpire to announce: Game, set, and match to Mr. Ferris. Those amenities were not provided humble qualifiers, but Mitchell Ferris didn't give a damn. He'd made it. He was in! He was in the draw for the Men's Singles Championship at South Orange, New Jersey, a $125,000 tournament. Having played the satellite circuit for two years without getting past the quarters anywhere, today he had made the big jump.

There was a smattering of applause from a few idle bystanders as he shook hands across the net with his defeated rival. Nobody much showed up for these matches; except for the players and their mothers or girlfriends. Nobody cared, Mitch Ferris mused ruefully. Usually, it was cautious tennis, each player afraid to make the error. He had hit out, played aggressively, charged the net. He was proud of the way he had won. On the computer ranking list, Mitchell Ferris was 247 in the world; his opponent, 90, so it wasn't a bad win. He grabbed a towel from the back of a chair and sat down beside the net post to dry himself. His dark, curly hair dripped with sweat; his lean, muscular body was soaked. He felt great!

The crowd, a euphemism, began to disperse.

A woman in tennis clothes came over. She wasn't young. Her legs had been good once, Mitch thought, but her face was dried out from too many summers, and probably winters too, in the sun. She had a badge pinned to her shirt and a pad and pencil in hand.

"Congratulations. What were your scores?"

"Four and two."

"That's very good."

"Thanks. I was on," he deprecated. She wasn't that old either, he thought. She had kept in shape, and according to her badge, she was a member of the club PR committee. He gave her his most boyish and engaging grin. "I really could use a little more practice on this surface. I'm not used to the slow courts. Would you like to hit some?"

"Sorry, I'm on duty. Some other time."

"Sure." He grinned. Old bag, he thought. In fact, this surface, a composition called Har-Tru, was perfect for him. It was what he played best on. Anyway, did she really think he wanted to *practice?* All he'd have to do was go a couple of rounds and she'd be bragging to her friends that he'd asked. And he wouldn't give her a second look. Ferris forgot about her as another of the spectators approached—a man, not a player or an official; Mitch knew them all.

"Nice going."

"Thanks. I was lucky."

"Didn't look that way to me."

Could he be a reporter? Mitch preened.

"I'd like to talk to you for a few minutes, Mr. Ferris."

Smiling brightly, the tennis player nodded as the man reached into his inside jacket pocket.

Police! Ferris gasped.

Reissig put his ID wallet back. "I want to ask you a few questions about a girl you used to know. May Guttman."

A light breeze ruffled the national flags marking the perimeter of the club grounds. The sun was bright, the grass green, and multicolored umbrellas dotted the grounds and terrace where lunch was being served. Mitch Ferris shivered; goose bumps broke out all over his body. He clenched his teeth and shook himself.

"May? . . . what about May?"

"She's dead. Stabbed. You didn't know?"

He frowned. "I read about it."

"That's all? You didn't try to contact anybody about her? Not even to ask about the boy? Your son?"

"Oh, God!" Ferris closed his eyes and pinched the bridge of his nose. "I read he's with her folks in Miami. That's right, isn't it?"

"Oh, yes."

"Thank God." He let out a deep sigh. "Well then, it's okay. I mean, I'm sorry about May, naturally, but there's nothing I can do."

"You haven't seen her recently?"

"We broke up over six years ago. We haven't seen or talked to each other or exchanged Christmas cards. Oh, God! I'm sorry; I didn't mean that. We were young. I was eighteen and she was seventeen when we ran away together. Neither one of us had any idea of what we were getting into, the responsibilities. She got pregnant right away. We weren't ready."

"You did know you have a son?"

"She refused an abortion."

"Did you bother to find out whether it was a boy or a girl?" Reissig thought of his own children—Anna was deaf, Robin retarded; he would not have given up one hour of one day of either of their lives.

"I didn't think she ought to have the child. It was her decision."

"So you walked out."

"I did what I had to do."

"How about money? Did you ever send her money for the child's support?"

"I'm not John McEnroe or Jimmy Connors. There's a big gap between those guys at the top and us. We're cannon fodder. Where I live it's a struggle to get from one tournament to the next."

"You were never curious to see your child?"

The handsome tanned face twisted into adolescent bad temper. "Give up, will you? It's none of your business. You're trying to make me out as some kind of monster. The kid wasn't even born when we split. This is the first time I've been on the East Coast since."

"Is that so?"

"Yes."

"When did you get here?"

"I came to enter Newport, that started on July Fourth, but I didn't make the draw. Hell, I never had a chance. It's on grass. I never played grass. They let me hit exactly fifteen minutes before going out to play the match. I never had a prayer."

"Did you contact May when you came East?"

"Why would I do that? I didn't even think of it. Anyway, I didn't know where she was. She could have gone to China for all I knew. She could have got married. That was what she wanted." The scowl deepened.

"Did she contact you?"

"How could she know I was here?"

"She could have read your name in the paper."

"The papers don't publish my comings and goings. I'm nobody. Look, Detective . . . uh, Reissig, I swear to you if I had known anything about May's death—how or why she was killed—I would have gone to the police. But I don't know a thing. So, if you don't mind, I've got to get to the showers; my muscles are cramping up."

"What were you doing Saturday night?"

Mitch Ferris got up, but the question stopped him from leaving. He mopped himself with a thick towel, but the sweat was already dry. He reached for the cable-knit sweater on the back of his chair and pulled it over his head. All of it added just about a minute for thinking. "I don't remember," was the best he could come up with.

"You don't remember what you were doing this past Saturday night?"

"That's the night she was killed, right? You're asking me for an alibi. I don't know what I was doing. I just happened to see her picture in yesterday's paper. Otherwise, I wouldn't even have known she was dead." Bad temper gave way to real anxiety. "You've got to believe me. I'm sorry for her, I'm *sorry*, but there's nothing I can do."

"You can reconstruct your movements Saturday night. You can tell me where you were and with whom. Or put me to the trouble of finding out."

"Yeah, yeah, all right. Let's see. Saturday I had a chance to get some good practice with a friend who used to coach me. He's the pro at the Rockaway Hunt Club."

The beat of Reissig's heart quickened. He knew the Hunt Club. It was very exclusive, very snobbish, and not five miles from the scene of the waitress's murder. Did Ferris realize that?

"I spent most of the afternoon out there working on my serve mainly. We had dinner and then I came back here to the motel."

Sooner or later it would have come out that he'd been in the vicinity of the murder scene, Reissig thought, so he was being smart to admit it. What choice did he have?

"You have a car?"

"A rental."

"What time did you leave the Hunt Club? And where did you go?"

"After dinner. Say, nine-thirty. And I told you, I came back here to my motel."

"And what time was that?"

"The drive took maybe a little more than an hour—say, ten-fifteen, ten-thirty. Then I went right to bed."

"The desk clerk will probably remember."

"I didn't stop by the desk. I had my key."

"Anybody at all see you? Did you talk to anybody around the motel grounds? In the parking lot? Did you have a nightcap anywhere on the road or before turning in?"

Ferris shook his head; he was looking very worried.

"Well, it's entirely possible that somebody you don't even know about saw you," Reissig strove to assure him. We'll check it out." He closed his notebook. "Sorry to have kept you from your shower."

Ferris wasn't so anxious to go anymore. "What time was May killed?"

"We don't know yet."

Frowning, the tennis player picked up his rackets and slowly started along the path to the locker room.

"Ferris?" Reissig called after him. "When's your next match?"

Ferris had to bring himself back from other concerns. "It depends on the draw. If I'm in the top half, it'll be Sunday."

"Good. I'll try and catch you."

The autopsy report on May Guttman came in that afternoon. According to the best medical opinion, she had died between nine-thirty and eleven-thirty on Saturday night. According to the testimony of her landlord, Charlie Harrington, Howard Baffler was sitting in his car in front of the house in Long Beach during that entire time.

Gary debated calling Mulcahaney. Once the autopsy report fixed the time of death, he would have checked out Baffler's alibi. Sure he would. It was both a procedural and a moral obligation. Mulcahaney's suggestion, he grimaced, no, her insistence that he had collared the wrong man had saved time and embarrassment. Baffler would be released with apologies and everybody was going to look good from the lieut' on down and even including himself. So, he owed her. As he had been the one to invoke professional courtesy, he should now observe it. He should admit that she had been right and compliment her. What about the new suspect? He bit his lip ruefully. Might as well tell her, she'd find out soon enough.

He hoped she wouldn't want to go with him when he went back to South Orange to see Ferris the next time. He knew damn well she would.

It rained heavily the night before. A typical summer storm: cloud to ground lightning, devastating thunder. Out in the open and particularly at the shore where Reissig lived, it had been terrifying. The children had been badly affected. Even in the city where most people were insulated from its violence, the intensity had been alarming. Water seemed to pour out of the sky and splash on the pavements. Gutters overflowed; sidewalks were partially submerged.

The next morning the air wasn't as fresh as usual after a heavy storm. It was cooler by a few degrees, but the humidity, even in the early hours, was high. It would get worse; that was the weather bureau's promise. As Norah walked down the steps of the station house and the half block to her car, she could already feel the wetness at the back of her neck and the inside of her thighs was beginning to chafe.

It hadn't rained as hard in South Orange, but enough to swamp the courts. By noon, the scheduled starting time for the opening round, machines had sucked the water out of the playing surface and everything was dry, bright, and in prime condition. The crowds, however, were thin—nobody of importance was due to play; in fact, the top names were finishing up in Washington, D.C., and in Kitzbühel, Austria, and wouldn't even arrive till Tuesday. Norah had been assured that Mitch Ferris would be present whether the matches started on time or not; he was required to be or risk default, so the trip would not be wasted. But she was pleased she would be able to see him in action, to observe him without his knowing.

She had no trouble finding a parking space and spotted Reissig waiting for her at the main gate.

For a moment he didn't recognize her. He saw a young

woman waving. She wore a mid-calf faded denim skirt flounced Western style at the hem and a plaid shirt, sleeves rolled to the elbows. Her dark hair was tied back and gleamed with auburn flashes in the sun. He didn't recall that her eyes were blue, such a very deep hyacinth blue.

"Hi," he said as she came up to him. "You look different."

"You don't look like a cop either."

They both laughed.

She examined the plaid of his slacks and compared it to her shirt. "We clash."

"Do you care?"

"Not one bit."

"I've got us passes so we don't have to be flashing our shields all the time," he told her, and taking her elbow, steered her to the turnstiles. He handed over the tickets and they pushed through.

The grounds had been spruced up and made festive. Freshly prepared beds of yellow early-blooming mums contrasted with masses of pink begonias and flaming sage. Colorful, striped tents covered the commercial enterprises, making the food and souvenir stands a part of the design rather than an intrusion.

"This is great." Norah looked around appreciatively. "I feel like a kid on an outing." She took a deep breath and exhaled slowly. "Anything new?"

Reissig shook his head. "According to his buddy at the Hunt Club, Ferris left there about nine-thirty, but he wasn't seen at his motel till close to midnight. A woman player on the tour was coming in herself at the time. She drove into the parking lot and picked him up with her headlights just as he was locking his car. She knows him and recognized him. There's no room for doubt. Also, Ferris claims, as I told you, that he hadn't seen May since they broke up, and they hadn't been in touch. On the other hand, her landlord insists it wasn't May's habit to take men upstairs but during the past three weeks she'd been breaking her own rule. That's just about how long Ferris has been East."

Norah considered. "Suppose he had got back to the motel at ten-thirty or thereabouts, could he have killed her?"

The timetable was fresh in Reissig's mind. "Obviously, he didn't go to May's place to pick her up because Harrington says she left at seven, alone in her car. Assuming they had a date and met somewhere, then drove together in her car to the lookout spot, it still had to happen sometime after nine-thirty because he didn't leave the Hunt Club till then. After the murder, he would have had to go back to wherever he'd left his car and drive like hell. At best it's an hour's drive and a lot more if traffic is heavy."

They reached the main scoreboard.

"He's on court nine," Norah noted and studied the diagram. "That way."

The match had already started. FERRIS VS SUND-GREN, the placard back of the umpire's chair read. According to the program, Sundgren was number twenty-two in world rankings. Apparently, nobody much cared about the outcome. Norah and Reissig had no trouble finding seats in the temporary stands. It quickly became evident that most of the few spectators were Sundgren supporters—a group of Swedes, all tall, all blond and enthusiastic.

Mitchel Ferris certainly answered the description Rose-anne Hurlock had given of the man her daugher had been dating—tall, dark, and handsome. Not very specific, but he was, Norah thought, the type a shy girl who had never had a boyfriend, who had never been flattered or sought out, could fall in love with and be completely dominated by. He was a glamorous figure in a glamorous sport, sought after by other women, and he had preferred her, Nancy. The question was—why had she kept his identity a secret? They had not been having an affair; the girl was a virgin at her death. On the other hand, why would Mitch Ferris have bothered with her? She didn't have looks; she didn't have money, that is, not real big money. She was an ordinary bank clerk.

What did she have to offer that the other women he met at tournament after tournament did not?

Norah was watching Ferris's movements, not so much his shot production but what he did in between points. He tugged at his shirt, twirled his racket, shifted his feet. Never still. Was he nervous because the match was going against him, or was it something else? After a while, she became aware that the cheers from the Swedish contingent were getting louder and more exuberant. A look at the score board told her why: their man had won the first set.

At the court change, Mitch Ferris slumped in his chair to one side of the umpire's and wiped the sweat from his face, his arms and legs. Looking around, he saw Gary Reissig in the stands. It was a shock. Not having heard from the detective since the day of the qualifying round, Ferris had convinced himself Reissig had lost interest. He felt a hot flash pass through him, then a chill. He noticed the woman with Reissig. Attractive. His wife? He tried to tell himself her presence proved the detective was not on official business, just a spectator, just curious because he had talked to Ferris. He didn't really believe it. Time called; he got up and walked to the opposite baseline and prepared to receive.

The first serve blasted by him. He missed it completely. A good ball, he should nevertheless have had it. He clenched his teeth and walked over to the left court to receive again. This time the ball was just as hard but he got his racket on it and hit it with a wild swipe and sent it sailing out of bounds. The Swedes were jubilant. God! What was going on here? He noticed that the woman accompanying the detective was watching him intently. He felt she had no interest in the game. His qualms increased. Had Reissig come to arrest him?

Once again he got ready to receive. He forced himself to concentrate, watch the ball. It broke sharply and bounced high to his forehand; he lunged, hit down on it, and slammed it down the line for the point.

He wasn't going out a loser.

Ferris stopped fidgeting. He crouched low and waited for the next serve. It catapulted across the net low to his backhand; he chipped it crosscourt to his opponent's backhand. Thirty–all. After that, add-out, his advantage. Then his game. It was the first time that he had broken Sundgren's serve. As the players changed side, Ferris looked up at the detective and his lady. If he was going to be taken off the court in handcuffs, it would be as a winner. Only as a winner would he make headlines. It could be a big publicity break for him, but he had to win.

Each time he faltered, a look at Reissig and his companion forced Ferris to greater effort. The word spread through the grounds that the match was tight and an upset, albeit minor, was in the making. By the time the umpire announced game, set, and match to Mr. Ferris: 2–6, 6–4, 6–1, a respectably sized crowd had gathered and the applause was solid. Other players, tournament committee people who had ignored him earlier, now gathered around Mitch Ferris to offer congratulations. Sundgren was left with his very subdued group of countrymen. Triumphant, Ferris forgot the detective who had spurred him on to win. At the first break in the tide of adulation he remembered, but by then it appeared that Reissig and his friend were gone. Ferris's sigh was a gust of relief. He started the walk back to the locker room and grinned with pleasure as a couple of flashbulbs popped in his face and kids trailed shouting for autographs.

He took his time in the shower, accepted offers to buy him a drink, and came out feeling mellow and ready to go to watch the others work. Reissig and the woman were waiting at the foot of the small flight of steps.

"Congratulations," Reissig said.

"It was a very exciting match," Norah added.

Ferris had to make two tries before he could clear his throat. "Thanks."

"This is Detective Sergeant Mulcahaney from Homicide in Manhattan," Reissig told him.

Ferris froze. Nothing at all came out of him this time.

"Let's go and sit down." Reissig indicated the main club-house terrace.

Ferris had no idea how he even made it that far, his knees were so weak. All he knew was that at some point the three of them sat down together at a table overlooking a rolling sweep of lawn.

"I have bad news, Mr. Ferris," Reissig said. "Your friend at the Hunt Club confirms that you left at nine-thirty on the Saturday night, but you were not seen at your motel till midnight."

"I was there between ten-thirty and eleven. Closer to ten-thirty."

"You were seen coming from the motel parking lot at midnight."

For just a moment Ferris was confused, then his eyes and his face cleared. "Oh, that, sure . . . yes. I forgot. I was in my room ready to turn in when I remembered that I'd left my brand-new racket that I got from Fitz, my friend at the Hunt Club, in the trunk. I didn't want to let it sit there all night. Dampness would affect the strings. So I threw on slacks and a shirt and went out to get it."

"Why didn't you say so before?"

"It slipped my mind."

Norah picked up the interrogation. "Where were you a week ago Sunday, Mr. Ferris? That would have been the eleventh of July."

"I guess I was in Boston."

"Guess?"

"Yeah, sure. It was the next stop on the tour so that's where I would have been."

"But you weren't in that draw, either. In fact, you didn't even make the qualifying round."

Now he really heated up. "It was a mixup. I got left out by accident. Somebody goofed. I've applied for reimbursement of my expenses."

"I see. How long did you remain in Boston?"

"All week. I'd paid for the room."

"The shuttle to New York is handy."

Embarrassment gave way to fear. God, oh, God, *how much did they know?* "I had no reason to go to New York. And I can't afford to fly back and forth anyway. I stayed in Boston till it was time to come here. I came early to make sure there was no 'computer error' this time. I came by bus."

Norah didn't challenge it. "Do you know Nancy Hurlock?"

He shook his head. He didn't appear interested. If anything, he seemed relieved to be on something else.

"Suppose you tell us exactly what you did and where you were on the night of Sunday, the eleventh of July," Norah suggested.

Ferris turned from her and looked anxiously to Reissig. It was a measure of his distress that he should seek help there. Reissig, however, remained neutral. "I don't remember," Ferris replied. "Why do you want to know? What's it got to do with anything?"

"Nancy Hurlock was killed on Sunday, the eleventh of July," Norah told him. "She was stabbed to death in much the same way as May Guttman."

He stared. "I never heard of any Nancy Hurlock. I told you."

"Where were you that night?"

"I don't know. Stop asking. I don't remember. Oh, God . . ."

With a glance at Norah, Reissig broke in. "You don't have to answer any more questions. You have the right to remain silent. If you . . ."

That brought Ferris close to panic. "No, no, I want to answer, I do." He began to twitch, the nerves throbbing in his shoulders and passing down his arms into his lean, strong, tennis player's hands. "Don't arrest me. I'll tell you whatever you want to know. I was . . . hanging out with the guys. We had dinner at the Locke-Ober then we went disco-ing at Metro First. I think we wound up at Spit. And that was it. I didn't turn in till maybe four A.M. I mean, I wasn't playing, so what did it matter?"

"Who were these guys you were hanging out with?"

"Well, there was a bunch of us. We kind of picked up and lost guys as we went along. It was that kind of a night."

"Give me some names. The names of the guys you had dinner with."

"I can't. I was drinking—a lot. I tied one on. I swear, I don't remember."

"No problem. I suppose a lot of players in this tournament were in Boston too. We'll ask around."

"No! No. I don't want you to do that. Please." He shifted to arrogance. "I don't appreciate a couple of cops snooping around and asking questions about me from my friends. I want to know what you're after. I want to know what's going on." He pointed at Reissig. "First you turn up and accuse me of killing my ex-wife who I haven't seen in six years. Now you," he pointed at Norah, "want to involve me with some girl I never heard of. I want a lawyer."

"You're entitled to one," Norah assured him.

"Look, I have a suggestion," Reissig offered. "We have a witness who saw May with a new boyfriend. Are you willing to participate in a lineup and let him look you over?"

"No!" Ferris pulled back violently, eyes bulging. "It wasn't me. I've told you that over and over . . ."

"If he fails to identify you, that'll be a big point in your favor."

"Suppose he makes a mistake? Then what? No way, no way I'm going to take that kind of a chance. Think I'm crazy?" His breath was coming in short hard gasps as though he'd played a long, exhausting point. "I think I'm getting the picture. You don't have enough evidence to arrest me, so you're trying to trick me. Well, the answer is no. I'm not going with you. Don't you understand? I won today! I won! I'm still in the tournament. I have to play my next match the day after tomorrow. I can't go with you."

"Mr. Ferris, if the witness fails to identify you, you'll be back in a matter of hours."

"I don't believe that." He was leaning forward, poised on the edge of the wire mesh chair, and looking around wildly.

"Where are you going to run, Mr. Ferris?"

"I'm not going to let you take me," he shouted.

A group at a nearby table looked around curiously.

Norah stared back at them till they self-consciously averted their eyes. "All right, all right, Mitch," she soothed. "Let's forget everything but the night of May's murder, this past Saturday. If you can just clear up the time discrepancy, tell us where you were between ten-thirty and midnight, you're off the hook."

The high color drained out of his face. He was gray as a sick man, his breathing shallow, his eyes hooded. "I can't. They'll kill me."

He spoke low so that both Norah and Gary Reissig had to strain to hear, but they understood.

Norah sighed. "Were you buying or selling?"

He bent his head low. "They'll kill me," he mumbled.

"So you deal," she said. "And on the night May Guttman was killed you were meeting your supplier. That missing hour and a half you spent with him. Is that right?"

Ferris started to shake.

"You might as well tell us the whole thing," Norah urged quietly. "You're out of business anyway. We have to report to Narcotics; they'll be watching every move you make from now on."

He looked up. "You won't take me in? You'll let me play my next round?"

Norah answered first. "I think that could be arranged."

Reissig nodded. "Okay by me."

Both knew that in his present condition he didn't stand a chance.

Still Ferris resisted. "I can't give you the names of my customers. I wouldn't be able to stay on the circuit."

So they were players, Norah thought. Who else? She knew drug use was rampant among athletes, tennis players not excepted. Yet in the ambience of open air and sun and wind, of young men and women apparently bursting with health, running, sweating, and straining for excellence, it saddened her. "How about your supplier?"

"Smiley." He paused then added bitterly, "I've never seen him smile."

"That's the only name you've got?" Reissig asked.

Ferris nodded. "I was supposed to meet him at Erin's Pub, that's a bar on Sixtieth and Second, but he was late. The bartender will remember me; I had an Alka-Seltzer while I was waiting.

"Okay, we'll check it out."

"You're free to go," Norah told him.

He got up like an old man. He walked slowly, each step tentative as though he wasn't sure his legs would support him, and headed toward the clubhouse. Suddenly, he stopped, shook his head and changed direction. He left through the main gate.

"Will he hang around to play the match?" Reissig wondered.

Norah nodded. "Sure. He doesn't know he's already lost."

Chapter _____
_____ TEN

The media smelled out the involvement of a "star" tennis player—the first time Mitch Ferris had ever been so designated—and drugs with the murder of an ordinary, obscure waitress instantly elevated to "glamorous." Casting out in all directions for information, they also became aware of the interest of Manhattan Homicide. It wasn't difficult to make a connection between May Guttman's stabbing and the murder in Central Park, as Captain Jacoby had anticipated. Headlines intimated what the accompanying story cautiously qualified: a multiple murderer at large.

The stories began by underscoring the similarities between the two crimes, dwelling particularly on the facts that both victims were young women in their twenties, and that both had had their throats slashed. Then they pointed out that the women were single and unattached. Neither had been sexually molested. Both girls had driven their own cars, and both lived on Long Island. Afterward, the writers scrupulously noted that although Nancy Hurlock lived on the Island, she had been killed and her body discovered in Manhattan in Central Park, while May Guttman, the glamorous waitress, was found near the beach in Far Rockaway. With equal care, they added that Nancy was outside her car, the car doors locked, the keys in her purse; while May was inside, the key still in the ignition.

Most single women read only the scarifying headlines.

The women who drove alone to and from work read the stories but weren't reassured. Young housewives in suburbia, for whom the car was a lifeline to the world outside, recalled a series of "thrill murders" a year back and were frightened. Generally, the public, sweltering in record-breaking heat, continued to drive out to the parks and the beaches vaguely hoping the media was overreacting in order to sell more papers. At the same time, they mistrusted the police assurances that everything was okay. Why didn't the cops *do something?*

Even Norah found herself shaken after reading the stories. Two murders did not make a series. She was certain of one thing only—if the stabbings had been committed by the same man, he was no psycho. He knew exactly what he was doing.

The number seven train rattled overhead on the elevated track curving from Long Island City along Queens Boulevard through the center of Sunnyside. As the cars clanked on the rails, the tracery of their lights was reflected in the rain-streaked window of Homer's Bar and Grill. Loitering behind one of the pillars supporting the structure, Frank Salgo waited impatiently for them to pass so he could see his mother again.

Magda Petrus was perched on a stool at the bar talking and laughing with the customers. She wore an off-the-shoulder black peasant blouse with a wide black lace collar. Even from across the street the whiteness of her smooth skin was a dazzling contrast, the fullness of her breasts tantalizing. Homer Petrus, behind the bar, was making up a drinks order for the waitress. When it was completed, he went around to join his wife. He put a hairy arm around her waist and leaning down kissed her in the hollow of her neck and shoulder.

Frank cringed.

Petrus's flabby lips nuzzled Magda's bare flesh; he rubbed the stubble of his dark rough beard down, down to the edge of her blouse. He defiled her in public!

Frank grew hot with shame and rage. Stepping out from beneath the shelter of the elevated tracks, he let the soft rain cool his flaming cheeks. His eyes, however, remained fixed on the scene behind the plate glass window. His mother looked tired, Frank thought, her smile and her gaiety forced. He hated to see her in that place night after night seated at that bar, a shill for the men to buy drinks. She didn't do it for that reason, he knew. Homer said they didn't have enough time together, that he wanted her company. But he was using her. She tolerated it, because she had no choice.

It wouldn't go on for much longer, Frank thought. He'd get her out of there soon, real soon, away from those men, away from that slob, Petrus. He would take her anywhere she wanted to go. He'd look after her as he always had since his father left them. Frank was thirteen when Stefan Salgo walked out, but he had known what to do. It was just a lousy break that he got sent up for a year, he should have gotten a suspended sentence. He would have too except that the woman judge wasn't a Family Court regular and was out to look good. Bitch. He didn't blame his mother for getting married while he was inside. What else could she do? She had to live. It made him sick to see Petrus touch her.

She was so beautiful! Frank thought. Her hair was black without a touch of gray, her skin without a line, cool as marble, her lips full and red—she never used lipstick. When Frank kissed her he felt the soft membrane of her mouth, not a sticky, flavored cosmetic. Her body was slim, her breasts full and firm without the need of a bra for support. Frank sweated. No girl he had ever known equaled her, not even Nancy. At the thought of Nancy, his blood cooled; he was soothed. She had been sweet, gentle, and pure. He had cared for her; he had felt safe with her. But she had come between him and his mother. He couldn't allow that. He couldn't allow anyone to do that. The memory of Nancy in the park with the picnic cloth spread out on the grass filled him with a bittersweet regret. As to what happened after . . . he felt the familiar nausea and dizziness: forget it. Block it out, he told himself, and fixed his mind on his mother again.

When he was eleven years old, Frank had seen her naked. The bathroom door had been open and he had just walked in and seen her lying in the bath. She hadn't been embarrassed and, after the first moment, neither had he. They had smiled at each other; he had lingered for . . .he had no idea how long. Then he had turned and walked out. They had never spoken of it, but he had never forgotten.

The rain, no more than a fine mist when Frank first took up his post, intensified. It turned into a downpour. It soaked through his clothes to his skin, but Frank Salgo wasn't aware of it. He watched as Homer Petrus put his fat hands on Magda and kissed her full on the lips, flaunting his possession in front of the other men.

Frank trembled.

Wasn't that son of a bitch going to be surprised! The kid he'd thrown out into the street was going to stick it to him. The kid he thought was dumb was smarter than he was. Soon he would have money, all the money in the world, and his mother would be able at last to leave Petrus. Petrus was laughing now, but he would be crying later. He would be the one standing out in the street in the rain—alone. Maybe he would throw him a couple of thou', Frank thought, throw the slob a few bills and make him eat them! Frank threw his head back in silent laughter and the rain streaked down his cheeks like tears. A woman passing looked him full in the face. His dark eyes narrowed dangerously and he stopped laughing to return the look. She lowered her head, pulled the umbrella down almost to her shoulders and, eyes on the pavement, scurried by.

Salgo forgot about her before she forgot about him. All he could think of was going inside to grab Petrus and slam him to the ground. His stepfather was bigger, but he had his knife, a slick, sharp knife, and he knew how to use it; it wouldn't be like the other time. It would make him feel good to hold it to Petrus's bulging Adam's apple; it would make him feel real good to see his stepfather squirm, watch his eyes pop; hear the gurgle of fear start at the base of his throat and rise to foam through a gaping mouth. But it would be dumb. Dumb. He could wait. In the end it would be much more satisfying. Meantime, Frank glanced at his watch; it was nearly time.

And he wasn't going to her empty-handed. He had a present for his mother. It was only a token of what was to come, a reminder that she could count on him always to take care of her, and a peace offering. It had been easy to pick up and he had intended to sell it and bring her the cash, but somehow he just hadn't been able to get rid of it. Frank clutched the brown paper bag around the top so the casual observer would think he was carrying a bottle, but neither he nor Magda Petrus drank.

Across the street in the bar, Magda looked at the clock back of the counter. She said something to her husband, then to the men around her, and slid off the stool. As she passed, Petrus reached out and smacked her on the buttocks.

Everybody laughed.

Frank Salgo choked scarlet on his rage. He would make the slob pay, he swore to himself. He watched as his mother went from the bar to the tiny vestibule and then unlocked the door separating the apartment section of the four-story building. He watched and waited till he saw the upstairs lights come on. It was just eleven and Homer would not lock up till one A.M. There was plenty of time.

He crossed the street and rang the doorbell. It was answered almost immediately.

Lila Cestone entered the main offices of the J. C. Marshall Company in Hempstead promptly at eight-thirty. She smiled and said good morning automatically, noting who was in and at work and who was not. Passing directly to her desk in the area reserved for junior executives—and separated from staff and public by a low, glass partition—Lila knew her progress was being watched. She enjoyed the attention. She was very much aware that her inner transformation had pro-

duced an outer one. There was a glow about her that had
never been there before.

Lila Cestone was twenty-nine, closing fast on thirty. She
was diet-slim, her features finely drawn, her hair a silver
blonde, wispy. When the light shone through, it imparted a
waiflike fragility totally out of sync with her true character.
Not that it really mattered, for any illusion of beauty would
be spoiled when the deep gouge on her left cheek was observed. A birthmark, it had been slight and barely discernible in her youth. Through the years it deepened and spread a
spider's web, a fine tracery of which she had been very self-
conscious. As soon as she'd been able to afford it, Lila had
undergone cosmetic surgery. Unfortunately, the doctor had
not been qualified, and when the bandages came off, she was
confronted by a scar that was smaller but deeper and
puckered like a string pouch. A mark more disfiguring than
before. Somehow, Lila Cestone had come to terms with her
appearance, but she refused to try surgery again, to take the
chance of further, greater disaster. Instead of turning her
face sideways to show the right profile, Lila made a point of
placing herself so that her visitor could not fail to note the
scar.

My dueling scar, she called it.

But she didn't need to do that anymore, Lila mused, as
Jerome Landauer, a senior v.p., came by. She let him see
the good side.

"Morning. Hot enough for you? The rain last night didn't
cool us off much, did it? I'm sending down for coffee. Want
some?"

He knew she never took it. It was a ruse to come around
and talk. She decided to surprise him.

"Yes, I would like some, thanks. Dark, no sugar." She
smiled, picked up the nearest folder and bent her head over
it.

"Ah . . . Lila? Why I came over . . . I have a couple of
tickets to the ballet at Lincoln Center tonight. Actually, I
was supposed to take a client but he can't make it. I know
you like ballet, so . . . how about it? Want to go?"

Landauer wasn't that far above her, still . . . he could do her some good. She considered. Not that much good, she decided.

"Sorry, Jerry. I'm busy tonight."

The day passed quickly for Lila. She was able to trace a missing shipment of men's shirts delivered to the wrong branch and then charged to yet another. Normally, she would have stayed to straighten out the invoices and the billing. Let it wait for tomorrow, she thought as she walked out precisely at five. She wanted to get home to bathe and change before picking up her date. He didn't have a car and it would have been ridiculous to make him trek all the way out to Glendale Village by public transportation.

Lila Cestone had always been self-sufficient, living alone, selecting privacy over companionship. She knew that women alone were at risk, but she was not afraid. Neither was she foolhardy. She read the papers, but she didn't think a mass murderer was on the loose. It made great copy. In Lila's opinion, the victims had been incredibly careless. She felt sorry for them, but one way or another, they had brought it on themselves. She had no qualms about driving alone, though perhaps she was a little more wary than usual. She looked out of the peephole of the front door to her ground-floor garden apartment to make sure no one was loitering. She locked up carefully after herself and moved swiftly to her car. Once in, she relocked the door before starting the engine. She had no intention of picking up hitch-hikers or even of rolling down her side windows. That was why she had air conditioning.

Lee Schoenberg drove placidly along his regular delivery route. He had just crossed the Nassau County line from New York and made a left on Peninsula Boulevard. He was a middle-aged man, overweight, of limited intelligence, content with his humdrum job. In fact, he savored its solitude and monotony. The loneliness was an insulation from others smarter and more ambitious, a protection from any kind of competition. He lived alone for the same basic reason—an inability to conform to another's needs and desires. He was content. As the social climate changed, anxiety invaded his serenity. He had enough grasp of reality to realize his job made him a target for crime, for robbery and even murder in much the same way as a taxi driver, bus driver, or trucker. He even thought of quitting, but who else would hire him? What else was he fit to do? Then one day, on this very same stretch of road, a white German shepherd had jumped up into the milk wagon and refused to leave. Lee had coaxed and threatened and shouted, but she stayed. And with Lady beside him, Schoenberg was no longer afraid.

Though it was not yet dawn, the air hung heavy and still. Schoenberg felt stifled. He was already filmed with sweat. It would be a hot one, he thought, as he rolled along the broad tree-lined avenue toward number twenty-nine—two regulars, two skims, one half-and-half. Suddenly, Lady began to growl low in her throat. Lee was instantly alert. There was no traffic. He looked up and down and all around: the streets were empty, the houses dark. Nothing seemed out of order. But Lady was never wrong about an unfriendly presence. Lee slowed down, watching and listening. Then about a couple of hundred yards ahead a woman emerged from beneath the heavy canopy of leaves and out into the road and in the full glare of his headlights. She waved to him.

Lady threw back her head and began to howl.

The woman walked . . . staggered . . . toward him.

She was covered with blood. Blood made a collar around her neck and a broad stripe down the front of her dress. Above the bright scarlet her face shone luminescently; her silver hair was almost transparent. He threw on his brakes and jumped out of the cab. That was when he noticed the car pulled over on the shoulder, listing slightly with the driver's door open and apparently sprung. Where was the other car? Hit and run! Schoenberg thought indignantly.

The woman opened her mouth. "Agh . . .agh . . ."

He stopped where he was. Her throat was open, yet the

terrible, unintelligible sounds continued and the blood bubbled under her chin and foamed out of her mouth.

"Don't try to talk, miss," Schoenberg implored. "For God's sake, please, don't try to talk. You come with me. I'm taking you to a hospital."

He didn't know he was crying. The tears were streaming down his pudgy face and he didn't know it. He did know that he was sick, nauseated, and close to tossing his breakfast. It took every bit of his willpower to look at her, much less touch her. Nevertheless, Schoenberg stretched out a hand.

She took two more steps, but before he could reach her, she fell at his feet.

"Oh, my God." The timid milk driver quivered.

The dog wailed mournfully.

Lee Schoenberg swallowed bile and pulled himself straight. "You stay with her, Lady," he ordered. Then, leaving the dog to guard the woman, Schoenberg raced to his wagon, started his engine, and sped the quarter mile down the road to a bus stop where there was also a pay telephone. The Nassau Medical Rescue Unit arrived within minutes. Distraught as he was, Schoenberg had to admit they were fast. Nevertheless, by the time they arrived, Lila Cestone was dead.

Norah heard about it on the seven A.M. news.

It wasn't much more than a bulletin, but it underscored that this latest killing was similar to one committed less than two weeks before, that both women had had their throats cut in a particularly vicious manner, and that both had been killed in their own cars with the key still in the ignition. Then the clincher, this second murder had been committed within five miles of the other. That, Norah thought, was guaranteed to send spasms of fear through every woman living on the South Shore and plenty on the North too. By seven-thirty radio and TV newscasters had seized on the story as the feature for the morning and reporters were out in the street conducting interviews with young, single women.

"I used to think that once I got inside my car I was okay,"

responded an assistant buyer at Macy's on her way to work. "Now I make sure every door is locked, but I'm still scared to death."

The others said the same in various ways. Fear bred fear. Norah was angry. It was exactly why she'd been reluctant to accept the "one-killer" theory. She debated whether or not to phone Gary. She had no doubt that he had heard. Being close to the Nassau line and the connection to the previous case already accepted, he had probably requested permission to take a look at the scene. In which case, he was on his way, if not already there. Then her phone rang.

"Norah? Sorry to get you up. I wanted to tell you . . ."

"It's okay. I'm on my way to work. I heard. On the news. They're trying to link it to the Guttman murder."

"No way we could muzzle them." He sighed. "We didn't release this information, but she was still alive when the milkman found her. He hacked it, Norah. He left her with her neck partially severed and she managed to crawl out of the car, drag herself to her feet, and flag down the milk truck. Then, with help on the way, she gave up."

Like Nancy, Norah thought, and knew Gary was thinking that too or he wouldn't have mentioned it. He was suggesting a link between all three crimes, and the media would also, soon enough. She was surprised they hadn't already.

Norah sighed softly. "When you talk to her family and friends and the people she worked with, find out if she had a new boyfriend. Find out if anybody knows who he is, or if anybody got a look at him."

"I will." Gary paused. "Why don't you come out with me?"

"Thanks. I was hoping you'd ask."

Lila Cestone's people were out on the coast in Los Angeles; she had lived alone in the condominium development. She had been a pleasant neighbor, while at the same time keeping to herself. A private person. She'd had few visitors, no male friends. She went to the theater alone and had a season's subscription to the ballet but no one ever saw her come home from these events with a date. Such an occasion would have been duly noted. It was accepted by all in Glendale Village, in the section called Elm Tree Walk, that Lila Cestone was a successful business executive, and that she was entirely dedicated to her work.

It appeared she had not been sexually molested. So far, Norah thought, the pattern held.

"Before we go to her office, could we take some time to stop by the scene? Do you mind?" Norah asked Reissig.

"Sure, why not?"

It didn't take long to get there. Lila Cestone's brown Chrysler Le Baron had been towed to the police garage. The spot where it had been parked, including the point to which the victim had managed to half walk, half crawl, and then signal the milk truck, was roped off and the official "crime scene" notices posted—affixed to the ropes and tacked to the trees. There was no one around to enforce observance. Norah noted that few passing motorists were even aware of them. Then they merely slowed down and since there was nothing gory or titillating, they sped on by. Reissig pulled over and he and Norah got out.

It wasn't anybody's fault that the ground was trampled, that the chalk outline of the body position, at best impermanent on grass, was nearly washed out by the morning dew, or that the trail of the victim's blood had soaked into the bare earth. There were two or three dark spots where Lila Cestone must have paused in her desperate attempt to find help. It would take a downpour to eradicate those. And again Norah couldn't help but think of Nancy Hurlock.

"What time did the milkman find her?"

"Just before four A.M."

"I don't suppose there's much traffic here at that hour?"

"None, just about."

Even now there was very little, Norah noted. The road was broad and curving, heavily shaded by fine old trees; the street lights well hidden among the foliage. The houses were set well back and on this particular stretch widely separated.

"About her car—was it possible to tell whether she was driving?"

"The blood was predominantly on the driver's side and on the carpet beneath the driver's seat. The steering wheel was liberally smeared. She exited from the driver's side, sliding out from under the wheel."

"There was no doubt in May Guttman's case that she was the one driving?"

"None."

Norah frowned. "Maybe he doesn't know how to drive."

"So?" Reissig shrugged.

"It could explain why he had to use the victim's car; why the murders took place in relatively public areas. If he could drive himself, wouldn't it have made sense to use more secluded spots?" She pointed down the road. "That's a bus stop, isn't it?"

"Right."

Norah was groping, following one thought to the next on instinct as much as logic. "May Guttman was parked within walking distance of a subway station."

"Right." Reissig's eyes gleamed.

"And Central Park is certainly handy to public transportation." Norah visualized Nancy Hurlock dying within view of a thousand darkened windows.

"I think you're on to something; I'm not sure what."

Norah's excitement grew as she continued. "In each case he planned his getaway. That's to be expected." She was thinking aloud, a habit she had picked up from Joe. They had bounced their ideas, no matter how far fetched, off each other. That was what she was doing now, though she wasn't aware of it. "What this means is that none of the murders could have been spontaneous. What we're dealing with here is premeditation in the full sense."

"You've always maintained that."

"Till now I wasn't really sure."

Chapter

ELEVEN

The sun had set but it brought no relief from the heat. Captain Jacoby's office was stifling, the window was closed on Jacoby's theory it kept the heat out. A fan on top of the filing cabinet merely distributed the fetid air. He had long since shucked off his shoes, but his feet were only the more swollen. His pudgy face was oiled with sweat, his small eyes half closed, the slits barely discernible in the folds of flesh. He sat motionless in the wooden armchair to further reduce the body's energy heat, looking as though he were dozing. But he didn't miss a word of Mulcahaney's report.

And she knew it.

"Lila Cestone had a new boyfriend. Just like the others."

The interviews she and Gary conducted at the J. C. Marshall Company, a nationwide chain of retail stores, had been productive. Whereas Nancy Hurlock had been a bank teller, May Guttman a waitress, both anonymous jobs, Ms. Cestone had been an executive of a major corporation. She had been under close scrutiny, both by those under her who were dependent on her good opinion and her moods for their welfare, and by those above who were constantly judging her performance. So both office staff and management not only were eager to talk to the detectives but also had something to say.

"She was seeing somebody new and very special," Norah

went on. "That's got to be more than a coincidence. Also, she was killed in her own car."

The tip of a white-coated tongue flicked out and wet Jacoby's thick lips. "You've changed your mind apparently."

"Yes and no," Norah replied. She was sweltering. She wanted nothing so much as to stride over to that window and fling it up and lean out to get a breath of fresh air, for heaven's sake! "What I didn't buy was the idea of a psycho killing at random. Now the pattern is taking shape and it's consistent." She ticked off her points. "Nancy Hurlock's mother admits Nancy told her she was seeing a man, and that she was deeply in love with him. Detective Reissig, out in Far Rockaway, talked to May Guttman's landlord. He saw a strange man coming out of her place late at night on several occasions only a short time before her death. The people at the J. C. Marshall Company confirm Lila Cestone had a steady, recently acquired."

Now Manny Jacoby opened his eyes, appearing fully awake for the first time during the discussion. "Somebody see him?"

"Afraid not. But she talked about him," Norah replied. "Casually. Just to let them know around the office that she had a man. Bragging, but not openly. Never said much outright—not who he was or what he did, was never seen with him. The impression was maybe he had some kind of menial job she was ashamed of. Or he might have been younger than her. But there was no doubt she was turned on by him."

"A mystery lover, huh?" Manny Jacoby pulled up in his chair. "The same man romancing three different women? Concurrently?"

"It's easier to accept than each victim just happened to have a new man in her life at the time she was killed."

Jacoby fixed Norah with a steady, penetrating stare. Criminals and cops had quailed under it.

Norah planted her feet slightly apart, raised her chin, and met it. "Apparently his initial encounter with Nancy was accidental, but it could have been engineered. Picking up

May Guttman at the diner would have been a snap. We don't know yet how he connected with Lila Cestone."

"You mean he deliberately selected each one of these women?" The laser stare went right through Norah. "Why?"

She raised her chin higher. "Give me a chance to find out, Captain." It wasn't a plea, but a challenge.

Now that it was agreed the three stabbings were linked, Norah was given freedom to investigate in Nassau as well as the five boroughs. Realistically, there were no new leads anywhere. The alibis of the two suspects in the Guttman death—Howard Baffler, her steady, and the tennis player, Mitch Ferris—were established for the time of the third murder. Baffler had been on the road, remembered at a trucker's stop outside Washington, D.C., and Ferris had been celebrating at the USTA's gala ball at the Roosevelt Hotel, which hadn't broken up till four A.M. He was constantly in the company of friends and fellow players.

The vehicles involved in each of the crimes had been given microscopic examination and no trace of an unknown passenger turned up.

Again Norah agonized over the familiar questions: what did these three young women have in common? Why had they been chosen first to be courted and then brutally killed?

They were young: the age spread no more than eight years.

Each was single.

Each owned and drove her own car.

In classic cases of multiple murders, the victims were usually linked by profession—prostitutes the common target. But these young women were decent, hard-working; their jobs dissimilar. Sometimes, looks were the clue—the victims might remind the perpetrator of his mother or of a girlfriend who had betrayed him. But these girls were not lookalikes: one was brown-haired and mousy, another a flashy redhead, and the last a sophisticated blonde. They shared no physical disability, no distinctive mark. What did that leave?

Some shared experience? Norah wondered. Maybe they'd

served on a jury together and bore the responsibility for a verdict; and now the killer was exacting revenge. Also, a classic link. Norah checked it out. She asked at the places where the three had worked: they would have had to be excused to serve. As far as she could discover, not one of the three had ever been called.

How about some secret knowledge? Witnessing a crime? Being involved in the commission of a crime? She still had nothing to go on; she was only guessing.

She continued to work with Gary Reissig but days passed without tangible results and Reissig was able to spend less and less time with her. Finally, he was forced to give other cases priority. Norah knew her own time on the case was limited; soon the captain would lose patience and pull her off too.

As a change of pace, Norah decided to fulfill her obligation to Father Boylan and try to trace the stolen chalice when she got back to the city each evening. She began by studying the pawnbrokers' lists of recently pledged items. There was nothing remotely fitting the description. She hadn't expected there would be; she had told the priest so. The only hope of recovering the chalice was in the off-chance the thief had not offered it to a known fence, from whom he wouldn't get much anyway, but had managed to sell it to some antique shop or a private citizen who would not recognize it as a church item or suspect it was stolen. Possible but not likely. If, as Father Boylan believed, the thief was someone local, then maybe he had tried to sell it locally. It was one long shot on top of another, but she had promised to try. So with Our Lady of Perpetual Help as the center, Norah laid out an area for her search starting south from Fiftieth Street and moving up into the Sixties and east from Lexington Avenue over to First. Most of the shops stayed open in the summer till eight to appeal to after-work shoppers so it was easy for Norah to stop in two or three places before going home. The job was routine and she had time to think of other things. She began to wonder why Adrian Gourdine didn't call. She reviewed their date; actually, it had been more like a negotiating session. He had made a case and she had indicated she would consider and deliver a decision. She had expected that he would contact her, and prepared herself for a skirmish, but he didn't call. Nothing happened. She felt let down. Then she decided this was part of the game—the way Gourdine played it.

Norah canvassed the antique shops for nearly a week. Her last stop on Friday, a golden August evening, was a very small place on First Avenue near Sixtieth, not too far from Our Lady of Perpetual Help. The store was narrow and dark, not at all prepossessing, but by now Norah had learned not to prejudge; some of the dingiest holes had yielded the most glorious and valuable treasures. So she squeezed her way inside amid an assortment of furniture, china, brass, and silver from a mixture of periods. There was a brass headboard and a set of bentwood chairs, all in prime condition; a burnished bronze of Romulus and Remus and their wolf mother, a popular subject in Victorian times; a beautifully faceted Venetian chandelier. Glass vases and dishes and bonbonnières were arranged on shelves. In back of the stacked plates of an elegant dinner service, she spotted a dull gleam.

"What's that?" Norah asked the proprietor.

He was a big, flabby man in too-tight pants and a shirt open to the waistband, revealing the inevitable collection of golden chains amid graying chest hair and pale, flaccid skin. Dark suntan makeup and an improbably even auburn tint of his coarse hair and mustache contrasted ludicrously, making it difficult to gauge his age. He stepped forward with a certain deference, which barely masked haughtiness. "May I help you, madam?"

"Yes, please. That goblet. May I see it?"

"Certainly, madam." He reached and took it down. "It is a very fine replica of a piece by Benvenuto Cellini. Unfortunately, it is in brass rather than gold." With ceremony, he handed it to Norah.

She turned it, examining it. Father Boylan's chalice had no such artistic pretensions, but it was real gold. "Yes, I see." She handed it back. "I'm looking for something on this general order but in eighteen karat." From her shoulder-strap handbag Norah took out a photograph of the chalice Father Boylan had given her.

The dealer took out a pair of half glasses and perched them near the end of his bulbous nose. "Is it stolen?" he asked.

Norah sighed. "Yes." She showed him her badge.

He hesitated. "The article was offered to me, but I didn't buy it."

Norah's blue eyes flashed. "If you suspected it was stolen you should have called the precinct," she chided.

"I know that, and I did." He pursed his lips in righteous annoyance. "I even attempted to hold the young man while I went in the back to call. I told him I had to consult my associate before making an acquisition of that size. The precinct didn't answer. The phone rang and rang. While I waited I heard the front door close. I ran out, but he was gone and the chalice with him."

Norah frowned. "You should have called anyway and reported the incident."

"I did. They took the particulars."

"Over the phone? Nobody came to see you?"

"Nobody."

After all, what could you expect? Norah was annoyed and frustrated just the same. With the tremendous case load of the robbery detail, detectives simply couldn't put in an appearance at the mere report that someone was trying to sell goods that might or might not be hot. And if the detectives had come, they wouldn't have contacted her—she wasn't officially on the case. Still, hope flickered. "When did the incident occur?"

"Two, two and a half weeks ago."

And nearly went out. Too long, much too long. "Can you be more precise? Try."

"I am trying," he replied with asperity and squeezed his eyes shut behind the half lenses. "It was the day I took Tiffy, my Yorkshire terrier, to the vet. I was waiting for the call. Turned out she needed a hysterectomy and she had it the next day. That was the twenty-third." He opened his eyes and smiled. "She came through just fine."

So the thief was here on the twenty-second, Norah thought, ten days exactly from the time of the theft, and he had still been trying to peddle the loot. Hopeful. On the other hand, two more weeks had elapsed and it was very likely he had finally managed to get rid of it. Still, she hadn't expected to get even this close. "Can you describe the man?"

"Young, thin, dark hair, olive skin. Not bad-looking, if you like the sulky type." He drew a forefinger across the dyed mustache and sniffed disparagingly. "Dressed fancy, but I knew him for what he was."

"What do you mean? What was he?"

"Angry. Young, angry, and dangerous. I don't know what's wrong with the young ones today. They're filled with hate. Consumed by rage. No matter how fairly you deal with them, they resent you; they resent what you have; they don't care how hard you worked to get it. They want to take it from you. They come back and burn your place down. Or they wait for you in a dark alley and stick a knife into your gut. Even if I hadn't suspected the piece was stolen, I wouldn't have dealt with him. Certainly not for a church item."

"How did you know that's what it was"

He raised his eyebrows disdainfully. "The cross was engraved on the base. Here," he pointed to the spot on the photograph—small, but distinctly recognizable.

How had she missed it? Her mind just wasn't on this job, Norah thought; she was going through the motions but holding back from a real commitment. She had to do better, particularly since that engraved cross almost eliminated any chance a legitimate buyer would have accepted the chalice. "Would you recognize the young man if you saw him again?"

The antique dealer took off his glasses and replaced them in his shirt pocket. His myopic eyes were glazed, his face ashen under the dark makeup.

"No," he said.

She knew he was lying. He was afraid, afraid of a stranger because he was young.

Norah left disappointed, but hopeful too. Father Boylan's hunch the thief would try to dispose of the chalice locally had been right. It was a big jump to Father's next assumption—that the thief was also Sister Therese's killer. Still, it wouldn't hurt to go back and review the file. She knew only too well the stacks and stacks of reports compiled by the battalion of detectives that canvassed the streets after the nun's murder. She had been over them many times already. What could she possibly discover that she had missed before? Clearing the murder of Sister Therese would mean a lot to her personally, Norah acknowledged as she started back to her car. It would exorcise some ghosts; lighten the load of her guilt for Joe's death, though not remove it completely—that could never be.

It took a while to locate the reports she was after and get them signed out. By the time Norah left the One-Three and got back uptown it was nine o'clock and dark. As she approached her front door she noticed a man loitering at the building entrance. There was no doorman; the door was locked and each tenant had his own key, but one was always at risk in the process of unlocking and entering. Like any civilian, Norah was in the habit of making sure no suspicious stranger lurked ready to push in after her. So she held back to see what this stranger was up to. He had his back to her and was browsing in the window of the shop on the corner— a ladies' shoe shop. He was tall, conservatively dressed, but

Norah wasn't taking any chances. She shifted the bundle of files from her right to her left and opened the flap of her handbag, feeling for the butt of her revolver.

"I'm a police officer," she announced. "Can I help you?"

"Yes." He turned sideways, pointing into the store window. "What do you think of the red sandals? Or do you prefer the snakeskin pumps?"

"Adrian Gourdine! What are you doing here?"

"Waiting for you. What else?"

"Why?"

"Weren't you supposed to get in touch with me?"

"Was I?"

"That's what I understood. It's been over two weeks."

"Has it?"

"I thought you'd forgotten me." His look told her he knew perfectly well she couldn't.

"I haven't had a chance to discuss the matter with Lena and Jake, Mr. and Mrs. DeVecchi. They're still away."

"I see."

"When I do, I'll let you know." Why was she so defensive?

"You're a busy lady. I've been trying to reach you, but you're never home or in your office."

"I'm sorry." She shook her head with annoyance: why was she constantly apologizing? "As I said, I have nothing to tell you."

"Do you really think that's what I'm here about? Waiting on your doorstep for two hours?"

Norah smiled and relaxed a little. "All right, no. I don't think you're here about Toni, but I haven't given you any other reason."

"I'm interested enough to come around anyway."

"That's very nice and I'm flattered, but the answer is still no. I'm not in the market."

He lifted an eyebrow. "If that's the way you want it." He shrugged. "At least let me give you a hand with all that stuff."

"I can manage."

"Norah, for God's sake, I've been waiting out in the street for two hours. Let me carry your things upstairs and see you into your apartment. You could even give me a drink. What would it hurt?"

Norah felt herself blushing. The man had a way of making her feel awkward, naive. He also made her blood surge. She didn't like either sensation. She put the papers into his arms and took out her key.

Upstairs, he put the load down on the desk as she indicated. While she went into the bedroom, he went into the kitchen and fixed drinks—not having asked what she wanted, or where anything was. He poured out the only drink she kept in the house, white wine, and when Norah came out handed her the glass. She sat in the armchair. He sat across from her. They sipped.

"It's a nice wine," he commented, "but don't you get bored with it?"

"There's beer, if you prefer."

"Fattening."

Moments passed.

"Have you eaten?" he asked.

Norah shook her head and knew instantly it was a tactical error.

"Why don't we send out for something?"

She gestured toward the desk. "I've got all that to get through."

"You're so very dedicated."

"Is there something wrong with that?"

"Nothing. Unless it's a defense mechanism."

She stared. "You don't know anything about me."

He got up instantly and went over and stood in front of her. "I'm sorry. I had no right to say that. I apologize. You're absolutely sincere about your work. I do know that. In fact, I'm jealous."

"Jealous?"

"Hurt, maybe is what I mean. My pride is hurt that I've

made so little impression on you that you're not willing to give up a couple of hours poring over reports to be with me." The soft lips twisted ruefully.

That, at least, was honest, Norah thought. She replied with equal sincerity. "It's not that, Adrian. You've made an impression. I'm not ready to make a commitment."

"Who said anything about a commitment? All I'm suggesting is that we give each other some pleasure. What's wrong with that?"

"It's not for me."

"You don't know till you try. You could use a little fun."

Norah sighed. "It's less than a year since my husband died."

"You want me to come back in three months, four months, what?"

Norah put the glass aside and got up, striding to the door. "Goodbye, Adrian."

He stayed where he was. "I've done it again, haven't I? I've offended you."

"You do it on purpose. It's your technique."

"It usually works." His grin was boyish, but the look in his amber eyes was anything but.

Chapter _____
_____ TWELVE

That should have been the end of it, but Adrian Gourdine performed another of his volatile reversals.

"I've never met a woman like you, Sergeant Mulcahaney," he said. "I don't know how to act with you."

"Don't act," Norah replied.

"Right, you're right. I respect you, Norah. Can't we be friends? Let's start over from the top. Okay?" He held out a hand.

Norah sighed, then walked over and took it. Mentally, she registered that though he had made the gesture, she had been the one to take the action of walking back to him.

Then he left.

He was a man who, once having made a play for a woman, could not take a turndown. Still, Norah couldn't help being intrigued. Adrian Gourdine was good-looking. The eyes that peered from beneath the overhang of reddish-blond eyebrows were unusual, not merely because of the amber color, but because they had a penetrating sharpness. His lips were thin yet sensuous. Maybe the facial hair was specifically intended to draw attention to those strong points. Norah hadn't seen any of his work, but she had no doubt that as an artist Gourdine was at least competent. She sensed he wasn't as dedicated as he made out; more talk than performance. He wanted it all, she thought, but he wanted it to come easy.

Norah had met men like him before—and women too. She didn't go for the type, yet she was attracted. There was an emotional pull.

Once again Norah put him out of her mind, or rather shoved him to the back of it and closed off the compartment. She fixed herself a ham and cheese sandwich, made a cup of instant coffee, took the snack over to her desk and got to work.

At one A.M., Norah leaned wearily back in the chair and closed her eyes. She had discovered nothing new, nothing her own earlier investigation had overlooked. As far as she could tell, the same three suspects still remained—the three pupils of Sister Therese who had moved out of the neighborhood without a trace. If she hadn't been able to find them with the full manpower of her special task force, Norah brooded, how could she hope to do it single-handedly now? And the difficulty was compounded because the school where Sister Therese taught had been converted two years before from a grammar, junior high, and high school for both boys and girls to an all-girl technical high school. Add another six months to that time lapse; it was hopeless. Forget it. Get on with the real job; admit she was using an old case to distract herself from the reality of the present. Almost a month had passed since Nancy Hurlock's body was discovered beside the lake in Central Park. Within that time two more young single women had been murdered. Only two weeks ago, Captain Jacoby had given reluctant permission for Norah to continue the investigation. Gary had been forced to drop out. She couldn't justify continuing on her own much longer.

Nevertheless, the feeling persisted that she was staring at something important in those old files and not seeing it. She went to bed and fell into a restless sleep. At a little after three she was awakened by a rushing wind. The curtains in the bedroom billowed, knocking down a bottle of her favorite perfume and smashing it on the floor. She leaped out of bed, turned on the light, and stared down at the spreading pool of yellow liquid. L'Heure Bleue. Joe had chosen it for her. It was the fragrance he loved best on her and this was the last bottle he had given her. Crying, she cleaned it up. She told herself her tears were out of all proportion, but she couldn't stop. She went back to bed with the scent pervading the room; she knew when she woke it would have dissipated.

With the wind came torrential rain. The morning came in gentle gray mist, cool for a change. It was a summer of extremes, Norah thought, suffocating heat broken by violent storms, a day or two of respite and then the pattern repeated. Her own emotions seemed to veer as drastically. As Norah dressed she could feel the oppressiveness of rising humidity. Her body was clammy. She felt depressed.

When she got to the precinct and walked into the squad room, Art Potts signaled.

"I know, I know," she said before he could speak. "He wants me." She also knew why. With a sigh, she knocked, and entered Jacoby's office.

"I'm not ordering you to drop it, Mulcahaney," Jacoby was uncharacteristically conciliatory. "Just set it aside. At this point in time you haven't got a damn thing to investigate anyway. Every lead has dried up."

"Things will start to move as soon as we locate the boyfriend," Norah insisted, but even to her own ears she sounded dispirited. "We've just scratched the surface, Captain. I'm talking to every single person who had any contact with Nancy Hurlock, May Guttman, and Lila Cestone. I don't mean only friends and relatives but local merchants, people who came to the house—repairmen, deliverymen. It's not conceivable that he dated the three women, each one for a period of several weeks apparently, and that nobody at any time ever saw him." The pep talk was for herself as well as for the captain.

Jacoby's fleshy lips were pressed into a tight line. He considered. Norah had a moment of hope, quickly extinguished.

"You've been on it too long already. I want you to give Lieutenant Winninger a hand on the Met Museum canvass."

Once you were assigned to something else, time and energy were preempted. The first case might nominally remain active, but it was quickly buried under the new activity. Gary was a perfect example: she hadn't heard from him for over eight days and that meant he was snowed under with other work. Norah let her disappointment show but she knew it would take a lot more to move Manny Jacoby. She cast about for something. . . .

"Suppose there's a fourth stabbing?"

It startled him. Sweat broke out and bathed Jacoby's fat face; his pate gleamed. "There's no reason to think there will be."

Norah's chin went up. "Or that there won't," she said. Now that she'd mentioned the possibility, she realized it had been in the back of her mind for a long time. She saw it wasn't a new idea to the captain either, so she didn't need to push it.

Manny Jacoby was a pragmatist. Manpower was low throughout the department. Every commander was in the position of using triage to allocate personnel. The long, meticulous probes, the leg work, the patient interrogations, all were a thing of the past. Results had to be quick or it was on to the next case. However, Jacoby knew if there should be another stabbing he would be severely criticized for having shut the investigation down.

He got out a much-used handkerchief from his back pocket and mopped his entire face and head. "If we had one single thing to go on . . ."

"Captain, we have." Norah knew she was gaining ground. "He's not a crazy. He's got a purpose. He *selected* those women. That's why he was so cautious about being seen with them and why he induced them not to talk about him, not to tell family or friends about him." Norah warmed to her argument. "Both Lila Cestone and Nancy Hurlock were lonely; neither had ever had a real boyfriend, had ever been courted. Wouldn't it have been natural for them to be bursting to talk about him, to boast, to revel, even to show him off? In fact, Nancy finally did confide in her mother, though she made her promise not to repeat a word."

"Because she was afraid her father would break it up."

"Right, but she could still have told her mother his first name and a little bit about him—what his interests were, what kind of work he did, where they went together. She didn't say one word about him at the bank and she would have gotten nothing but peer approval there. As for Lila, she scattered broad hints around her office, but without revealing anything specific. The waitress—she was another type completely. She'd been married and had a string of men friends. She was open about them. Everyone knew who she was dating. In fact, most of her dates were customers at the diner and knew one another. But nobody even saw this last one and she didn't talk about him."

Jacoby rested his elbows on the desk and pursed his lips. "Could we be dealing with coverup murders?" He referred to a series of crimes used to camouflage the principal crime, a crime that would point all too clearly to both motive and perpetrator.

"I didn't think of that," Norah admitted. Why not, she wondered.

Jacoby was pleased. He warmed to his own idea. "Which one of them do you think he was really after?"

"I don't know." Norah frowned. "If two of the victims were for cover, why did he need to date them? He could have killed any girl in her twenties or any girl of any age that came handy. He could have stood on a street corner or waited in a dark alley and reached out and stabbed the first young woman to come by. No, he had a specific reason for killing each one. Maybe each one knew something about him—something he'd done, a crime he'd committed ear-lier." It was not new ground. "But that couldn't be since none of them knew him till he sought them out . . ."

"Hah," Jacoby grunted. He was disappointed that his own theory had been shot down, but he had other things to concern him. "When you get it sorted out put it in a report, half a page, and leave it on my desk." He reached for a recently started cigar, stuck it in his mouth, and bent back to the work he'd been on before Norah's entrance.

But Norah didn't leave. "Maybe they were in some way part of the target crime. He killed them so that they wouldn't reveal what the crime would be. He killed them before."

"Before what?" Jacoby was impatient to get back to productive work.

"Before he committed it, the target crime."

"Which is?"

Norah had gotten this far by building from one assumption to the next, link by link. She believed that at last the pattern was taking shape, but there had to be one piece of hard, provable evidence to justify keeping the case active. She respected Jacoby's position, but she had reached the end of the chain. "I wish I knew."

He didn't order her out. Norah could see him squirming as he got rid of his shoes under the desk and settled himself to some hard thinking. He had liked his coverup theory, and it could be merged with Mulcahaney's idea that the principal crime was yet to come. If that should turn out to be some big jewelry heist, or a bank job . . . Jacoby indulged himself in a few delicious moments of fantasy. The next grade up to deputy inspector couldn't be achieved by dogged hard work, nor by studying and passing an exam, but only by appointment of the P.C. If he were able to head off something really big—an assassination? No, that would be too fantastic. Anyway, if he could head off whatever it was, he'd get his promotion. With plenty of fanfare he might even make it straight up to chief! On the other hand, if nothing came of it, and on his past luck it wasn't likely to . . . If it turned out the murders were committed by a crazy, and way down deep that was what Jacoby believed, who could blame him for looking into the possibility? And the next time Mulcahaney came waltzing in here with her cockamamie ideas he'd be real pleased to remind her.

"Okay, Sergeant, you go ahead and see what you can turn up."

"Yes, sir." Norah jumped for the door.

"Nobody else. I can't spare anybody else. Not Brennan, not Arenas, just you, Mulcahaney."

"Right."

"And Mulcahaney, I want to be kept informed."

"Absolutely, Captain." She got away fast before he could have second thoughts.

Jacoby slid down on the end of his spine, stretched out his legs and wiggled his toes.

Only three persons besides himself got off at Woodmere, two men and a woman. All were met and driven away within minutes. Alone on the platform, he walked to the end and found a telephone.

"Hi, this is Frank. I got off at the wrong stop. Come and get me."

He was lying. He had gotten off three stops sooner on purpose to make sure nobody she knew would see them together. There were fewer passengers on the Long Island Railroad at that hour of a Saturday evening in summer; it was more likely he might be noticed.

"Oh, hell!" Melinda Russel muttered. "Okay, okay. Stay where you are. I'm on my way."

So she didn't like it. So too bad, neither did he. His broad face was flushed. The dark stain of sweat on the back of his T-shirt was spreading. What had started as a challenge had become routine. The women were too easy. He got no kick out of the sex and little satisfaction. In fact, it was getting increasingly tough to perform. Even fantasizing that he was with her, with Magda, didn't help all that much anymore. It was beginning to worry him.

As he crossed the tracks to shelter under some fine old trees, he reflected that it was almost done. He had reached the final stage. Then he could stop faking it, stop sucking up to these babes. He had one more choice to make, the last, but she'd have to be just right or the whole thing would fail. He'd come too far to let that happen. He had narrowed it down to two—both younger than the others had been, one of them still in high school. Did that really matter? Both were good drivers and that was the main thing. Melinda Russel, Melie for short, was rich and wild. She never let him forget she was rich. Bess Zimmer was poor and greedy. Melie would do it for the thrill, Bess for the money. If he chose Bess, he'd have to provide the vehicle, probably. Actually, neither girl was exactly what he wanted. Each was too popular, had too many friends, talked too much. And he wouldn't be able to shut her up permanently till afterward. That made him nervous. He should look around some more, but he wanted to get it over. This weekend.

The glass door of Ma's Kitchen, a fast-food restaurant on Burnside, swung open and a blonde teenager came running out with a brown paper bag in her hand. "Mister? Mister! You picked up the wrong lunch."

Karol Dobriansky stopped, turned around, and frowned. "Please?"

She caught up with him. "You took the wrong lunch," she repeated, spacing the words out slowly and precisely because she knew his English was shaky. As he still didn't seem to understand, she thrust the brown bag at him. "Egg salad and coffee, light, no sugar. This is yours." With the other hand she took the bag he had paid for and carried away. "You took the turkey on white and coffee black." She was young, maybe sixteen or seventeen, pretty, even more so than usual because she was flushed from running. Her breathing calmed and she drew closer but as she smiled at Dobriansky she made sure to keep her lips closed.

"Ah, yeah . . . so." Dobriansky accepted the exchange with a smile of his own that was shy but showed his admiration. Every night at seven-forty-five, give or take depending on how the buses were running, Karol Dobriansky, immigrant, entered the fast-food store half a block down from the bus stop and picked up his night lunch. He had the same thing—the cheapest—every time, never varied so it was ready for him at the end of the counter next to the cash register. Dobriansky was coming from his daytime job in Far Rockaway—delivery boy at a supermarket. Tonight had been no different from any other night. He had entered the restaurant and gone straight to the takeout section where his brown bag was waiting. He never stopped to talk, principally because he was in a hurry, also because he was shy, mostly because his English was uncertain. He couldn't recall seeing two brown bags on the counter, but, of course, there must have been.

"Sorry," he said to the pretty girl. "Sorry." He tried to think of something to add, to hold her there.

"That's okay." She gave him the close-lipped smile and turned quickly back across the lot.

Dobriansky watched till she was inside the restaurant, then with a sigh he continued on his way to the warehouse around the corner. He was young too, twenty-two. Stocky, with mild brown eyes and wavy hair, he had country boy good looks, though the ruddy coloring that came from long hours in the fields had long since faded; all that was left was a round spot of red on each cheek that looked as though it had been painted on. He was a stranger in a new land and he was lonely. But he had no time to make friends, no time for girls. Economic conditions being what they were and he a foreigner, Karol Dobriansky appreciated his good fortune in having work. Particularly the night watchman's job. That paid good money for . . . nothing, just being there. In honesty, he didn't feel he earned the money. Americans did not appreciate the high wages they received, he thought, nor their working conditions—all the result of their strong unions.

As he turned the bend where Burnside became Sheridan, a stiff breeze made swirls of dust that stung the young Pole's eyes, but it was welcome on that sultry night. He had discovered, without real surprise, that poverty existed in America as everywhere else—but on a different level. Here, welfare recipients wiled away the hours in front of color television sets. The homeless were housed and fed three hot meals a day but did no work—though the streets were filthy and cleaning them might have been a way of paying for what they received. Americans lived for the things money could buy. Yet where he worked money was treated casually, almost with contempt. Bags of it were hauled in and tossed in heaps up in a room on the second floor ostentatiously alluded to as the "money room"; actually it was no more than a metal mesh cage. Loads were hauled in on Friday night and Saturday and left to be passed on to the ultimate destination, the Federal Reserve, on Monday. Dobriansky watched and was appalled by the lack of control. He could, he'd often thought, open the sacks by slitting the rope back of the seal and help himself at any time. He doubted anyone would notice the tampering.

He could probably keep doing it for a period before anyone became suspicious. Common sense dictated that somebody somewhere was indeed keeping account of what came in and what went out. Meanwhile he sat all alone with untold thousands—no, millions—all through the Saturday and Sunday nights, week after week. Of course he was tempted, but he would never touch a single bill. First, because he was honest—the money wasn't his. Second, he had gone to the job interview without expectation of being hired. The union had made a special exception for him. He believed he had been admitted to the union and hired as a gesture of sympathy by the rank and file here toward the rank and file workers back home. He would never betray that trust.

The Mercury Courier Service offices and warehouse occupied a two-story, cinder-block building facing an inlet of Reynolds Channel just over the New York city limits. The gate in the chain link fence enclosing the parking lot was locked, a normal precaution. Dobriansky noted the five armored vans parked to one side and two passenger vehicles, one belonging to the day security officer and the other to the manager. He let himself in, walked over to the office entrance, and rang the bell. Having done that, he inserted his own key and turned it once. The guard he was relieving would come take his key off the hook in the receptionist's cubicle and turn it on the inside. Some of the workers complained that this counterlocking was dangerous in case of fire; someone might panic, jam one or the other of the locks and everyone would be trapped. In fact, that kind of deadlock was illegal in New York, but out here it was standard.

Horace Ludlum must have been waiting just beside the door. "You're late," he snapped as he turned his key and yanked the metal door back.

With a sideways glance Dobriansky checked the wall clock: he was late by three minutes. He merely ducked his head. "The bus. . . ."

"Sure. It's always the bus. Why don't you buy yourself a car?"

The man resented him; maybe because he was a foreigner or because he had gotten into the union without a waiting period, or because he was young and Ludlum was old and riddled with arthritis.

"I'm sorry," Karol said.

Ludlum ignored the apology. "Everything's locked and checked out."

"Thank you, Mr. Ludlum."

"Mr. Archibald is still here. As soon as he leaves you can turn on the alarm."

"Yes, sir."

Ludlum grunted. The younger man's deference didn't make much of a dent in his hostility. "See you Monday," he said. "Try to be on time."

He left before Dobriansky could answer.

Stifling a sigh, Dobriansky went to the guard's office, took off his civilian jacket and put on the uniform jacket with the Mercury patch on the sleeve. He took a copy of *A Child's History of America* out of the desk drawer. Every night he studied a chapter; in this manner he learned about his new homeland while at the same time improving his English. Before settling down, however, he would eat. In the middle of his meal, Mr. Archibald, the manager, left. Before he could turn on the alarm system, the phone rang.

"Thor Security. Callaghan speaking. There's something wrong with one of your relays. A short probably. Don't turn it on. When you do your next round call us first and we'll hold till you get through and report that everything's okay. Okay?"

The breakdown was not unusual. It had happened before, frequently—too frequently in Dobriansky's judgment, but as long as the bosses were satisfied who was he to say? In the morning, someone from Thor would come, find the trouble, and make the necessary repair. Meantime, as long as all the windows and doors were locked, he had nothing to worry about.

Karol Dobriansky finished his sandwich and drank his coffee. He opened his book and settled in for a quiet night.

The special duty security officer reporting for work on Sunday morning found everything normal. The gate to the parking lot was locked as it should be. Routinely, he unlocked it and then relocked it behind him. At the metal door of the office, he inserted his key and turned it, then he rang the bell for the man inside to use his key. Nothing happened. He rang again. He pounded on the door. What the hell? He put his ear to the metal sheeting and listened. His heart was pounding so hard he couldn't have heard anything anyway. He looked around. It was seven-forty-five on a peaceful Sunday morning and nobody was around.

He had to let himself out of the lot and race three blocks to a pay phone on Sheridan. Patrol cars responded within minutes, but it wasn't till the Thor Security Systems man arrived that the accumulated force of police and detectives was able to get inside.

Records are made to be broken, Lieutenant Paul Hoggarth

thought as he stood amid the rubble of torn lath and fallen plaster in the money room staring up at the hole in the roof. Was it back in 1947 that the Purolator Security warehouse in Chicago was robbed of $4 million in cash? In 1978—he remembered this one with certainty because he had been one of the more than fifty detectives assigned in Queens alone—the haul was $5.8 million from a Lufthansa cargo hangar at JFK International. So far, the outstanding feature of this heist was not how much had been taken, but how much had been left behind. Money bags lay everywhere in disordered heaps. There must be records somewhere, and when somebody turned up who could run some kind of inventory check, Paul Hoggarth had a hunch this one was going to top them all. That meant the investigation wouldn't be in his hands for long. As word of the heist spread, specialists from the robbery squad and from the DA's office would converge on the warehouse, so would the FBI. The NYPD brass and FBI would snarl over jurisdiction. Let them, Hoggarth thought. He was tall, thin, forty-five, his features were sharp, his light blue eyes steady and clear. Unfortunately, his good looks were spoiled by the dour set of his mouth. Hoggarth had been around a long time and one thing he had learned was that you got ahead by keeping your nose clean. Insisting on the truth could find you flopped back into uniform for your pains. Let somebody else do the crusading. Anyhow, this case wasn't going to turn out so simple.

Hoggarth choked as a gust of wind sucked in through the hole in the roof and stirred up a cloud of barely settled plaster dust. He rubbed his eyes and examined the hole once more. The roof was of flimsy construction, tar-papered, not much of a barrier. Some kind of portable power saw could have done the job easily. That had been the way in. Bolt cutters had snipped the mesh of the money cage and that had been the way out. The money bags were hauled down the stairs to the loading platform where, logically, the getaway car must already have been backed up and waiting. It could have been a one-man job. The night guard—Hoggarth consulted his notes, Karol Dobriansky, claimed he had only seen one man. It could explain why so much of the loot had been left behind, it would simply have been beyond the ability of one man to carry it all away. One thing Hoggarth was ready to lay odds on—there had been help on the inside.

How else did the vehicle get past the gate?

Let the big shots figure it out, he shrugged.

When the first contingent of police had gained access, they had found Karol Dobriansky manacled to the stair railing, gagged and bound. He had been lying like that all night, he said, roughly from an hour after he had come on duty—nearly twelve hours in all. He had a runny nose, the beginnings of a summer cold, and with his windpipe blocked by the gag he had come close to choking to death. The ropes around his legs were so tight that circulation was impeded and he could hardly stand when they were loosened. His wrists were bruised and swollen. The twin spots of red on his cheeks were feverishly bright. He was in no condition to be interrogated, but he wanted to talk; he was eager to tell his story. Hoggarth was eager to listen.

He had come to work as usual, clocking in at 8:03 P.M. precisely. That, of course, was on record. Dobriansky told the detective about the call from Thor and explained the procedure to be followed during each security round. He had not had the opportunity to observe it even once.

"I am finishing my meal," the guard recounted, "when I hear . . . something. Not a sound exactly. Rather I am aware . . . of a presence."

He selected his words well, Hoggarth thought. Maybe being a foreigner, he took extra care.

"I look up from my book of history that I am studying and I see a man with his face covered by a lady's stocking. He is . . ." Again the hesitation. "Big." An open gesture of both hands indicated it was the best he could do by way of description. "He shows me a knife. He grabs me from the back, pulls me up against him, and holds the knife to my throat, and says he will kill me if I move."

"Then what?"

The night watchman sighed. "That is all. He must have hit me on the head because I do not remember anything else till I regained consciousness, and found myself chained to the stair post and alone."

"According to the Thor people there was nothing wrong with the alarm system. They don't know anything about any call to you last night. All they know is that you didn't turn it on."

"I spoke to someone on the phone. A Mr. Callaghan."

"They don't have a Callaghan."

Dobriansky was both bewildered and anxious. "I was instructed not to turn it on. It was nothing new. It had happened before." If that was true, Hoggarth mused, then why hadn't someone from Thor come around first thing that morning to look for the trouble and repair it? "You said you were eating when you became aware of a 'presence.' Then you said you were reading. Which was it?"

"I was eating. That was when I had the feeling that there was something wrong. But I didn't see the man with the knife till later when I was reading." Dobriansky winced and passed a hand over his eyes. "My head aches."

"Did your head ache last night?"

"No, sir."

"There was nothing wrong with you? You were in good health?"

"I had the start of a cold."

"Was there anything wrong with your ears?"

"No, sir." The young foreigner didn't understand where he was being led but he had a sick feeling in the pit of his stomach that he wouldn't like it when he found out.

"Then how come you only *sensed* a presence?" Hoggarth demanded. "How come you didn't hear the noise when they were cutting through the roof? How come you didn't hear it loud and clear and go to investigate?"

Chapter

THIRTEEN

Estimates of the size of the take fluctuated wildly from hour to hour depending on who was questioned. At first, the haul was pegged at $7 million, a large part of the money that had been picked up by armored cars from local banks and was due to be delivered on Monday to the Federal Reserve. Later it was revealed that a further sum had been collected from Aqueduct Racetrack, the Friday and Saturday handle amounting to $850,000. There were also sales receipts from various Queens and Nassau supermarkets and other businesses. None of the executives of Mercury could give precise numbers, but the total was mounting steadily.

A spokesman from the FBI–NYPD Joint Robbery Task Force of forty investigators stated that there appeared to be no clues so far, but the perpetrators *must* ultimately be apprehended because of the very nature and magnitude of the crime. Such a crime inevitably resulted in a falling out among the thieves, violence and murder. Inevitably, it left a trail of blood.

What that meant was that they didn't have much to go on, Norah mused as she studied the details of the heist, as intriguing to the police as to the public. Lieutenant Paul Hoggarth, head of the Nassau Robbery Squad and the first of the detectives on the scene, had suggested to a v.p. of the armored car company that security arrangements seemed to have been very lax in view of the huge sums being held. He questioned leaving a single guard in charge. The executive, Jeffrey Hurlock, replied that they had complete confidence in the security system.

The name danced in front of Norah's eyes. She looked again as though through a haze, shook her head till it cleared. The name remained.

"He wants you!" Art Potts's voice cut through Norah's concentration and she jumped to her feet to answer the summons.

"Have you seen this?" Jacoby demanded as soon as she came through the door. He had in front of him the inter-office memo regarding the robbery circulated to all commands. He handed her the sheet.

It was, in greater detail, the same report she had just finished reading in the newspaper. "Jeffrey Hurlock. He's Nancy's father, the father of the first victim."

"Right." Using an already soggy handkerchief, the captain mopped his sweaty face.

Why couldn't he open a window? Norah was already oiled with sweat herself. Stubborn and intransigent on some things, Norah respected Jacoby's quick mind. She knew she could skip directly to the bottom line. "If it was a one-man job, it wasn't the slasher."

"How do you figure that?"

"The slasher doesn't drive."

"We don't know that for a fact."

That he didn't drive was an inference based on recurring circumstances and Norah was convinced of it. She continued to build on it. "He would have had to hire a wheel man. If our theory is correct that he killed as an advance coverup, it's out of character for him to take on a partner."

Jacoby scowled. "Unless . . ."

Their eyes met and he didn't finish.

"I wish I could talk to that guard."

"Why not?" He made a quick decision. "I'll set it up."

"Thanks, Captain," Norah said quietly, but her eyes were bright and her chin thrust forward.

Karol Dobriansky rented a room in the Polish section of Greenpoint, Brooklyn, an enclave so ethnic that the store signs were in Polish, and if you asked directions on the street you had a better chance of getting an answer if you spoke Polish. It was not an ordinary furnished room but a room in the home of a family of five, the Pulaskis—parents, grandparents, and one child. Dobriansky was welcomed as the sixth member and this family now closed around the adopted son.

They were present in the old-fashioned, over-furnished parlor when Norah arrived on Tuesday, late morning, to question Dobriansky. She didn't ask them to leave. One of the first things she had learned was not to permit herself preconceived notions about any aspect of a case. Nevertheless, there were patterns that repeated so frequently they were taken for granted. One such was the "inside job." As the man on the inside, the night guard was an obvious suspect. Young for the job by forty years at least, shy, polite, he was anything but a stereotype. But that was no reason to exonerate him either.

Having studied the transcript of the official investigation by the combined task force, Norah was familiar with the guard's testimony. She intended merely to prove the discrepancies, aware, of course, they were sores already much aggravated as team after team had badgered and cajoled, going over and over his story. She intended to be circumspect, even gentle. She accepted the chair she was offered and a steaming cup of good, strong coffee. Then under the watchful eyes of the elder Pulaskis—the boy was at school—Norah began.

"Mr. Dobriansky, can you tell me how you got the job at Mercury?"

Dobriansky sighed. How many times had he answered that question? "It was through my friend, Vlatan." He turned and smiled at the younger Pulaski sitting beside him while the grandfather across the room nodded in vigorous confirmation. "I am, in my country, a master electrician, but here I can only work as an apprentice and even for that there are no openings at this time. So I look for any work that I can get. Vlatan hears of the job. It also requires union membership. I am in my country a member and at Vlatan's request, as a gesture of friendship, I am admitted here and given a letter of recommendation."

"I see. I understand that you, yourself, are confused that you didn't hear any sound while the hole in the roof was being cut. Portable power tools appear to have been used, but in the silence of a late Saturday night, with no traffic, even an ax or handsaw should have been loud enough for you to be aware something was going on. Have you thought of a reasonable explanation?"

His honest, country-boy face was flushed, but his eyes remained fixed on Norah. "No Miss . . . Sergeant." Then he looked down.

He was holding something back. Everybody in the city was afraid—the rich and the poor, the young and the old; everybody walking the streets or hiding behind a battery of locks. Fear had become part of daily living. It was a matter of narrowing it down to the specific angst. "Are you afraid they'll punish you if you talk?"

"Who?"

The men you let into the warehouse was what she wanted to say, but he had already been directly accused of complicity. "The robbers," she replied instead.

"I saw one man only and he was wearing a mask. I could not describe him. How can I be a threat to him?"

"You say this man stood behind you, one arm holding you in your chair while with the other hand he pressed the tip of a knife to your throat. Then you say you were hit on the head and rendered unconscious. Doesn't that suggest two men?"

"I saw only one."

"You 'sensed a presence' while you were having your sandwich." Norah quoted from his statement.

"Yes."

"It wasn't till later, while you were reading, that you were attacked."

Dobriansky nodded.

"When you 'sensed' there was somebody in the building why didn't you investigate? Wasn't that your job? Particularly in view of the fact that the alarm system wasn't turned on shouldn't you have been extra vigilant?"

"I did look."

"Ah. You didn't mention that to the other detectives."

"There was nothing to mention. Everything appeared to be in order."

"Only it wasn't."

He flushed. "I said it appeared to be."

The touch of asperity was a betrayal of his nervousness. "Did you inspect the entire premises? Did you do a complete round? Did you get Thor on the phone while you did it?"

He bit his lips. "You know I didn't."

"Isn't that what you'd been instructed to do?"

"It wasn't necessary." As soon as he'd said that, he realized he'd made a bad mistake because of course it had been necessary. "I thought I had imagined . . ."

"I see."

Norah paused as though she were thinking it all over. The younger Pulaskis, Vlatan and Danuta, and the elder, Grzegorz and Elisabet, showed their anxiety.

"How long between the time you imagined and the time you actually saw the intruder?"

"I don't know. When one is alone for so many hours time is difficult to gauge."

"There was a clock on the wall directly opposite your desk."

"I wasn't feeling well."

"Mm." Norah glanced down to the sheet in her hand

though she knew by heart what was on it. "You had the 'start of a cold.' Did it affect your vision?"

"I swear to the Blessed Lord and to the Holy Virgin Mary, to the Blessed Lady of Czestochowa that I had nothing to do with the robbery. Nothing."

"I would like to believe that, Mr. Dobriansky, but your story simply is not credible."

"It's what happened," he repeated doggedly and hopelessly.

Vlatan Pulaski, his landlord and his friend, placed a hand on Dobriansky's shoulder. He leaned over and murmured a few words that Norah couldn't understand. The night guard dropped his head and half turned away.

Pulaski waited for a few moments, when he saw that Karol would not speak, he addressed himself to Norah. "Karol is not hiding anything. His story is confused because sometime after his meal, while he was reading, he fell asleep."

Norah sighed softly.

Now the night watchman looked up. "Everything that happened is my fault. I am to blame. I cannot believe I allowed this terrible thing to happen. It is all my fault."

Norah gave him time.

"Never before have I fallen asleep on the job! Never. I swear on my mother's grave."

"That is the truth, Sergeant Mulcahaney, Karol is not the kind to take money and not do what he is hired for." Pulaski backed his friend. "He is a decent, conscientious worker."

"I fell asleep!" Dobriansky wailed. "I am so ashamed. I fell asleep and allowed robbers to enter and take whatever they wanted."

"Were you actually hit on the head and rendered unconscious or did you make that up?" Norah asked.

"No, no, that is true. Absolutely. It happened as I said. No, not as I said. I was asleep and then aroused. And when I looked up he was standing there."

"What did he look like?"

"He was big."

"Can't you do better than that?"

"Miss . . . Sergeant . . . He was wearing a stocking over his face. That is true also. I swear it on the head of my beloved sister."

"All right. Was his hair dark or light? You could tell that much."

Dobriansky frowned. "Dark."

"How tall was he?"

"I don't know. As soon as he saw that I was awake, he grabbed me and half lifted me out of the chair."

He was useless as a witness, Norah thought, but she was not prepared to give up. "Could there have been more than one man? Think. Think hard, Mr. Dobriansky, this is very important."

"I'm sorry. I just don't know. I'm sorry. Oh, God, forgive me. I'm so confused."

Norah sympathized. The man held two jobs and had surely been tired enough to fall asleep, but the sleep must have been abnormally deep for him not to hear the racket on the roof. "About your cold, had you taken anything for it?" Repeated in a slightly different phrasing, approached from another angle, a question might get a new response, which might in turn suggest another line of enquiry . . . "Did anybody give you anything to take for it—cold tablets, antihistamine, anything that might have made you drowsy?"

"No, Sergeant."

Norah frowned. His account was so garbled. The shamed admission that he had fallen asleep was not a truly valid explanation of his not hearing the sounds of forced entry. Surely if he were involved in the commission of the crime he would have prepared something more credible. "When did you start to feel sleepy? How soon after you clocked in?"

"Not long. Maybe half an hour or an hour. I can't say closer."

"After you'd had your sandwich and coffee?"

"Oh, yes."

"Did you bring your meal from home?"

"No. I picked it up at Ma's Kitchen, that is on Burnside Avenue just around the corner from the plant. I pick it up every night before going to work. They have it made ready for me." He stopped, eyes bulging.

"What?" Norah prompted. "You've thought of something."

"There was a girl. She came running out after me. She said I had the wrong lunch. She took my bag from me and gave me another."

"One of the waitresses?"

"Yes," he answered promptly. Then he had second thoughts. "No, wait, I thought so. She had a cap and apron, but her dress . . . her uniform . . . it was not the same as the others."

"Can you describe her?"

"Pretty. So pretty. Young, blonde, with short curly hair like a halo around her head and her eyes were dark, alive. She was about . . . so tall." He held up a hand to indicate she had come to just about his shoulder. "She was slender. When she smiled, she kept her mouth closed."

The girl had made an impression. "I don't suppose you kept the coffee container?" Why should he have? "This Ma's Kitchen, does it have a parking area?" Most places in the suburbs did.

"Yes."

"Were there many cars parked in it?"

"Three or four."

"How about trucks or vans?" Norah was feeling her way.

He started to shake his head. "Wait. There was a van. It was the kind without side windows. It was old." Once again Dobriansky searched for the precise word. "Dilapidated. Gray." He watched for Norah's reaction.

She was careful to show none. "I'll look into it, Mr. Dobriansky." Turning, she included each of the Pulaskis. "I'll do the best I can."

But hard as she tried, Norah couldn't pick up a trace of

the girl who had run out into the parking lot of Ma's Kitchen to exchange brown bags with the night watchman. There was no employee answering the description. No one remembered a pretty customer with short blonde hair and dark eyes either. The counterman confirmed that Karol Dobriansky was in the habit of coming in each night at around seven-forty-five to pick up his standard egg salad on white and coffee, light, no sugar. Since he was so reliably prompt, the order was made up and waiting for him. There were few takeouts at that hour and the counterman was certain that on the Saturday night Dobriansky's had been the only one beside the cash register. Reasonably certain.

Was Dobriansky lying? Was the blonde who had come running out of the restaurant a fabrication? Had there been a drug in the coffee she handed him?

Nobody had any recollection of a dilapidated, unmarked gray van.

The executive offices of the Mercury Courier Service were prestigiously situated on the thirtieth floor of the RCA building in Rockefeller Center. Access to the offices was more closely regulated than access to the money room in their warehouse, Norah reflected as she waited at the reception desk while the sleek brunette buzzed the inner sanctum. Thinking of the interview to come, Norah formed only a general impression of her surroundings: modern opulent with lots of deep-pile beige carpeting, abstract watercolors in aluminum frames on beige walls—a glossy front for a sloppy operation. Of course, this was where the sales were made and the contracts negotiated. When she was finally escorted to Jeffrey Hurlock's office by a less decorative but presumably more efficient secretary, Norah was so concentrated on what she wanted to develop that she failed to respond to the sweeping view of the Hudson from the picture window behind the vice-president's desk—much less to notice that the QE II was making a majestic passage upriver to her dock.

Hurlock bypassed formalities. He was barely polite.

"If you're here about my daughter again, Sergeant Mulcahaney, I don't know what more I can tell you. If it's about the break-in at the warehouse, I've already told the Robbery Squad and the FBI everything I know. Please check with them."

"Actually, it concerns both." Norah appropriated the client's chair and settled herself. "I believe the two are connected."

He had been prepared to protest whatever she said, to argue, deny, defend. But that threw him off balance. "What are you talking about?"

"I know that Nancy worked for you at one time." Norah threw the fact out like a baited hook.

"Briefly, yes, when she first got out of school. She didn't like it. She felt in one way she was being given preferential treatment, and in the other that she was not being fully appreciated. You know how children are." He sighed; it didn't mask his puzzlement.

"So she was familiar with the operation in the warehouse."

"She worked here, in this office, but, of course . . . yes, in a general way she did know the routine out there."

Norah let him work out the implications for himself. He did. Quickly.

"Are you suggesting that Nancy was a party to planning the robbery? That she was so besotted with this young man, whoever he was, if he ever existed, as to give him information that would make robbing the warehouse possible? That she would have been in league with her lover . . ."

"They weren't lovers."

He stopped in full spate of his indignation to remember the horror of his daughter's body as he had finally viewed it. "I never believed otherwise." Jeffrey Hurlock threw back his white head proudly. "You were the one who insinuated my daughter was having an affair. Now you're suggesting she conspired with some unknown man to steal from her own father. I've had enough of you, Sergeant Mulcahaney, and of the police. Please leave."

Norah didn't move. "You're drawing your own inferences."

"As you intend I should. I'm not going to say another word." Turning his back, Hurlock walked to the window and stared out at the splendid liner as she grew larger within the frame. He was no more aware of the sight than Norah had been.

"Mr. Hurlock, I believe Nancy was very much in love." Norah hesitated. She could quote Hurlock's wife, reveal that Nancy had confided in her mother admitting the romance, but she had promised not to do that. "Unfortunately, the man was using her."

Hurlock's back stiffened.

"He probed for information and Nancy told him everything he wanted to know, quite innocently I'm sure, and with no idea of the use he would put it all to."

Still Hurlock refused to respond.

"Then, after he got what he could out of her, he killed Nancy."

Even that didn't do it. She would have to go all the way, Norah thought and took a deep breath. "Unfortunately, I don't believe that your part in all this is as innocent as your daughter's was."

He couldn't ignore that. He turned slowly and when he spoke it was with the formal reserve of an executive conducting a board meeting. "What are you suggesting?"

He came over and stood directly in front of her pointing a finger down at her. "Are you implying that I was somehow in league with my child's killer?"

"No, Mr. Hurlock. But I do wonder why you hired Karol Dobriansky."

"I didn't hire him. I'm the executive vice- president of this company. I don't hire night watchmen."

"You did interview him."

He scowled. He made a great show of thinking back.

"You're right. I'd forgotten. It seems our personnel manager was out sick and we were in desperate need of a watchman so I saw him."

"And you hired him."

"Yes, yes, temporarily and dependent on the personnel manager's okay."

"Why? Mr. Dobriansky is not qualified. He's had no experience. He's not even a citizen."

"Now you're questioning my judgment. He was recommended by the union and he has his green card."

"And so you felt confident to leave this one man, this stranger to our ways, who is still learning the language, to stand guard over $12 million." That was the latest figure given out by the FBI.

"I had confidence in our security system."

"Misplaced," Norah commented wryly.

"I don't need you to tell me."

"I also find it difficult to believe that nobody has an accurate account of the moneys held. I'm told there have been discrepancies in the past regarding the amounts taken in, held, and then delivered, and that the insurance company had to make up a loss on at least a couple of occasions."

"You can be sure that the insurance company made a thorough investigation and must have been satisfied with our procedures."

"Moneys appear and disappear on your books as though they were written with vanishing ink."

"So now you're an accountant, Sergeant? It's none of your business. You find my daughter's killer. That's what you get paid for."

Norah looked straight at him. "Don't you already know who that is?"

Whatever tremor shook him inside, it didn't show. "There is no connection. None."

"It was so easy for the money to be taken. You allowed it to be easy. You almost invited break-ins."

Hurlock clenched his teeth.

"Whose idea was it?"

Leaning down, Hurlock flipped the intercom switch. "Get me the police commissioner," he told his secretary.

"Whose idea was it to use the break-ins as coverup for fraud?" Norah persisted. "For steady, methodical embezzlement from a failing company? Who thought of it?"

Hurlock kept staring at his phone, waiting for it to ring.

"Was the first break-in genuine? Did it suggest the scheme? Were the subsequent robberies setups? Including the last one? Which were real and which fake? Wasn't the slow bleeding of the company enough? Did you get impatient for the big score?"

Hurlock put his hand on the switch again. "Cancel the call," he said.

"Were you in it alone? Were you the originator? Did you get caught by someone in the company and have to take a partner, or did one of the other executives conceive the idea and when you discovered it, you demanded a piece of the action?"

"The break-ins were genuine. All of them. I . . . we . . . had no part in any of them."

Norah didn't press him to reveal who else in the company had been part of the embezzlement scheme. She didn't probe for conspirators within the insurance company or Thor Security. The robbery and fraud division would ultimately uncover all that. "But you deliberately made it easy for robbers. You deliberately fostered the laxity that made the job attractive. You hired Dobriansky because you thought that as a foreigner he would be all the more easily gulled."

Hurlock's eyes were brimming as he met Norah's at last. "How could I know that some monster would latch on to Nancy for the information he could get out of her and then kill her? Kill her the way he did . . ." Tears ran down, making runnels on his wide face. "Leave her to die a little bit at a time."

"He was after the money. Just like you," Norah said
softly.

From then on Hurlock cooperated. He turned over lists of
present and past employees. Norah let the FBI pore over
them; she reasoned that if the killer-robber had worked for
Mercury or Thor he wouldn't have needed Nancy to tell him
about the procedures, particularly the manner in which the
alarm was monitored. He wouldn't have needed the other
women either: not May Guttman to supply information she
got from her truck driver dates about delivery schedules. He
wouldn't have needed Lila Cestone whose employer, the J.
C. Marshall stores, used both the Mercury pick-up service
and the Thor alarm system, to advise him when the largest
sums were likely to be held in the warehouse, and to confirm
that the alarm was still operating in the usual manner Nancy
had described. Norah continued to try to identify the perpetrator. She sought a clue among the belongings of the
victims. She worked doggedly and with the prescience of a
killing yet to come. Every time the phone rang, whether in
the squad room, at home, or in the places she searched,
Norah jumped.

She was looking among the possessions of the dead
women for some letter or note, some memento of a date—a
matchbook cover, a parking stub, a theater ticket—anything
that might indicate where the two had been together. As the
youngest, Nancy should have been the most likely to have
such a keepsake, but in fact Nancy had kept almost no senti-
mental clutter of any kind. Maybe because she'd never had
any.

Surprisingly, May Guttman, with so many men in her life,
turned out to be the maudlin one.

"She's got stuff dating back to her high school senior
prom!" Gary Reissig marveled as he tore off the tape from
one of the boxes stored in the Harringtons' basement. With
the Mercury Courier Service warehouse robbery and the

possible connection to the slasher murders, he had been returned to the investigation and had joined Norah in the second-floor apartment overlooking the ocean. "Look at this."

Norah sat beside him and together they opened the large, worn album. It began with May's own baby pictures and ended with those of her son. In between, May appeared in various stages of her adolescence and young womanhood, always smiling and always with her arm linked through that of a different young man—the current boyfriend.

"I don't suppose *he* let himself be photographed," Reissig commented as they turned the pages to the end of the album.

Norah wasn't listening. She was totally concentrated on the pictures of May's child—infant, toddler, little boy. He reminded her of Mark, the five-year-old she and Joe had adopted for a brief time and been forced to give up. She turned the pages slowly, remembering. Suddenly, there were no more pictures, only blank pages. She felt a clutch at her heart and a great wave of sympathy. Those snapshots were a recorded history of a mother's love. They told Norah that May had sent her child away not because he was an encumbrance, nor a responsibility she resented, but out of real love, knowing it would be best for him. After that, the waitress had had no more joy in mementoes, no heart for recollection.

Norah closed the album and gently set it aside.

"Anything in the rest of the boxes?"

Reissig shook his head. Something had touched Norah, he didn't know what, but he strove to dispel it. "Listen, it's nearly lunchtime. Why don't we knock off and relax? We could go to my place. It's just over the bridge."

"Your place?"

He grinned. "I'm a widower. I have two children and my mother-in-law keeps house for me."

"I'm sorry. I didn't know."

"Millicent is a very nice woman. We get along great."

Norah laughed. "Are you sure it won't be too much trouble for her?"

"I told her I might be bringing you. She's looking forward to meeting you."

"Then I'd be very pleased."

Gary's house was a huge, fine old place in an unfashionable pocket between Far Rockaway and Inwood, Rundown and needing a paint job, it was set on a large plot with ancient shade trees and a lawn that needed mowing. None of that mattered. As soon as the battered station wagon pulled into the cracked driveway, the children came running down the porch steps hand in hand shouting welcome to their father, laughing with joy. It wasn't till she got out of the car and approached that Norah saw the boy, Robin, was unhealthily overweight and uncoodinated—he moved with a jerking motion on his right side. Retarded, she realized with a shock. The girl, Anna, smaller and younger, who was leading her brother, called out eagerly. "Daddy! Daddy, you're home!"

Her voice was too loud, rough; the sounds guttural, produced with difficulty.

Because she couldn't hear her own voice, Norah thought. She was deaf. She stole a look at Gary, but he only had eyes for the children as he hugged them and held them close. "I brought you a visitor." Now he beckoned. "These are my children." He was very proud.

Millicent Crouse welcomed Norah and made her feel at home. The lunch was served on the shady back porch. It was an hour of pleasure that passed too quickly. It ended with a message for Norah. *Call in.*

She used the kitchen phone and when she returned she was no longer smiling.

"It's happened," she told Reissig, and he had no need to ask what.

Chapter

FOURTEEN

On the telephone, Norah had asked Art Potts one question about the latest slashing: what kind of vehicle had the victim been driving?

His answer: an old, gray, unmarked van.

So she and Reissig sped the short distance along Lido Boulevard, crossing a series of causeways out toward Jones Beach. Aptly called the Loop Parkway, the road was built on a sand spit between channel and sea and was all part of the Robert Moses system of highways and beaches. Japanese pines were planted along both sides to stop erosion and they stood like wind sculptures crafted by past storms. Patches of marram grass on the dunes undulated in a light breeze and the scent of wild scarlet rugosa roses in their last bloom of summer blended with the tang of salt spray. The sun blazed high in a cloudless sky. Reissig's station wagon was not air conditioned, but Norah was aware neither of the heat nor of the cooling breeze, and Gary's full attention was on getting to the scene fast. Both spotted the location from a quarter of a mile away by the line of police cars. They parked at the end of the row, got out and walked.

The victim was lying on the ocean side of the road underneath a pine, her form almost completely covered by a thin layer of sand. Had the killer tried to hide her? Why? The place was deserted enough, and no such attempt had been made any of the other times.

"There was a heavy onshore wind last night," Reissig explained as though Norah had spoken aloud. For further confirmation he pointed to the van listing off the shoulder of the road and the sand that had accumulated in certain crevices more than others, indicating the direction the wind had blown, a high wind that had passed unnoticed in the city. Norah noted the rear wheels of the van were deep in the sand as though they had spun over in a futile attempt to get back on the road. Probably that explained the second variation from the pattern—the distance of the murder scene from public transportation. If this murder was part of the series, then it should have been committed close to a subway line or bus route. But with the van stuck, the killer had not had that option. It was about time he ran out of luck, Norah thought.

Would he have looked for a ride afterward? No, she decided. He would have avoided being seen and perhaps remembered. Late at night or early morning, this road would have been empty, but in case of a rare car the killer would have sought cover. Still, the nearest available public transportation was the Long Island Railroad in Long Beach and that was a long, long way to walk. Somebody was bound to have spotted him trudging. Would a public appeal do any good?

Pursing her lips, Norah gauged the distance from the open door on the driver's side of the vehicle to where the dead girl lay—right arm outflung, head nestled against her armpit and left hip raised slightly. The sand would have to be sifted for a possible trail of blood, but it looked to Norah as though the victim had tried to escape, flung open her door and run. He had caught her and killed her where she now lay. She went over for a closer look.

Theodore French looked barely old enough to have graduated medical school, much less completed internship and joined the medical examiner's office. His movements were precise and swift; he seemed to know what he was doing. Norah considered the girl. She was about five foot three and very slim, the fragile slimness of youth. She wore tight jeans and a hot pink T-shirt that hugged small breasts. Her hair, a mass of close-cropped curls, was still encrusted with sand—a silver-blonde color that glinted like mica in the sun. She answered the general description Karol Dobriansky gave of the blonde in the parking lot. He had mentioned that she had kept her lips closed when she smiled. They were not closed now. What in life she had tried to keep hidden, the rictus of death revealed. The pretty girl had crooked front teeth.

Norah stared at the collar of dark, coagulated blood. She had seen that same band before, most recently around Nancy Hurlock's neck. As then, the lips of the wound were dried and clearly discernible. Norah sucked in her breath. The shape of the wound was curved.

"She was stabbed from the back," she told Reissig.

"Yes. Like the others."

"No, not like the others." Norah frowned. "Nancy Hurlock's wound was straight across. She was attacked while facing her killer."

They stared at each other.

"Why didn't you tell me?" Norah demanded.

"I thought you knew."

"I didn't view the other bodies," she snapped. "And I didn't read the autopsy reports," she admitted sighing. "I thought, I just took it for granted, that since they were killed in their own cars and by having their throats slashed . . . Dear God, how could I make such a mistake?"

"I didn't know about Nancy Hurlock," Reissig tried to show her he too was at fault. "I didn't know she had been cut from the front."

"It was up to me to tell you."

"So we both missed it. I don't see that it makes all that much difference."

Norah thought long and hard. "Maybe not. Could be that having stabbed his first victim while facing her, he found it awkward. After all, she did live through the night and someone might have discovered her and even saved her. So he could have changed his style."

"Sure." Reissig was anxious to reassure Norah. Also, going back to a theory of more than one killer meant starting all over again—nearly. In honesty, he didn't think the detail was of real consequence.

But Norah continued to worry. "This girl was killed while trying to get away. Outside her car. He had to chase her, catch her. So it was only natural to grab her and pull her backwards and hold her while he drew his knife across her throat. But May Guttman was killed while they were sitting together in her car and so was Lila Cestone."

"When he pulled the knife, it would have been instinctive for the victim to turn away."

Norah wasn't satisfied. "Doctor? Have you any idea how long she's been lying here?"

"The sand acts as a preservative," French muttered. Then he looked up. "As a guess, anywhere from twenty-four to seventy-two hours. Sorry."

"Shouldn't a passing motorist have spotted her in all that time?" That question was for Gary.

"He would have thought she was sunbathing or picnicking; people do that around here." He was gray under his tan. "We don't look for murder out here."

Norah watched as he walked away, down to the edge of the strand, and stood staring out to sea. She let him go alone. This area of small towns and resort beaches was his home. He had been born here and was raising his children here. What happened had touched him in a way that she, having grown up in the city, could never fully comprehend. Meanwhile, she picked up the victim's purse. There was a driver's license in the name of Bess Zimmer. The address was in nearby Inwood. The van, however, was registered to a Stanley Belkin with a Cedarhurst address. The towns were intertwined, part of the Five Towns group. Inwood was the poor relation.

The Zimmers lived in a typical lower-middle-class neighborhood. The houses were old and modest, but carefully and lovingly maintained. They were surrounded by small yards also devotedly tended, every foot cultivated. Flowers abounded, but there were also vegetable plots and sometimes grape arbors to sit beneath for the evening meal. No mass development, it had grown naturally over the years, each house individually built and cherishing its nonconformity. The Zimmer house was like the rest only in the economic value it represented.

Norah and Reissig climbed the porch steps. She had barely touched the bell when the door was flung open.

As soon as she saw them, the eagerness died out of Yolanda Zimmer's eyes. "Yes?"

"We're police officers, Ma'am," Reissig said.

"My baby! My baby! Where is she? Have you found her? What's happened to my Bess?"

The woman was slim, deeply tanned, blonde hair sunbleached; in her mid-forties, on good days she looked younger. Today was not one of them.

"May we come in?" Norah asked.

Mrs. Zimmer's face sagged. She reached a hand behind her toward the stair banister for support and stepped back into the tiny hallway. "Where is she? Where's my child?"

Quietly, as gently as she knew how, Norah told her.

"No!" The mother shrieked and then slowly sank down to the lowest step, crying. She cried with anger as much as sorrow. Norah and Reissig waited it out.

"Those kids, those lousy rich kids," she managed at last between strangled sobs. "It's their fault. They got her hooked. Oh, God, I knew it would end like this."

"I don't understand, Mrs. Zimmer," Norah said.

"She gets bussed to that fancy high school in Lawrence. Those kids get more for an allowance then I earn at the five and dime. They're snobs. My Harry works for Lilco. He reads meters. That makes us peasants."

"You think they introduced Bess to drugs?"

"Think! I know. Oh, God, I know! At first, I thought she was sick. I mean, really sick. She slept till noon. Walked around like a zombie. I didn't know what was wrong with her. God, was I naive! So, I grounded her. I told her no more coming in at three and four in the morning. Curfew at twelve. And on school nights, no dates at all. Then I caught one of her so-called friends passing the junk to her through her bedroom window."

Norah and Reissig exchanged glances.

"Who was the friend?" Norah asked.

Mrs. Zimmer shook her head. She no longer sobbed; the tears were drying, but the bitterness was far from quenched—would never be. "I couldn't find out. I blame the school and the police—you people, you . . ." She pulled herself to her feet. "How can you let these criminals, these pushers, hang around the schoolyards and corrupt the children? How can you let them get inside, into the corridors, to sell to the children? How can you allow it?"

Neither of the detectives could answer.

"Every pusher is a murderer. A murderer. *A murderer!* Kill them. *Kill every one!*" Yolanda Zimmer screamed.

"Please, Mrs. Zimmer, you'll make yourself sick." Norah put a hand on her shoulder.

"You think I care? I don't care. I want to die too."

"We're here because we want to catch the man who did this to Bess. We need your help."

"What good is catching him going to do? She's gone. My baby . . ."

"He's killed others."

"Yeah, sure he has. That's what I'm telling you. Every pusher is a murderer."

"Then help us get him."

Teetering on the edge of another outbreak Yolanda Zimmer took a deep breath and the tears overflowed into the gutters of her ruined face. She fumbled in her pants pocket and brought out a crumpled ball of Kleenex. "How?"

Norah spoke quickly, matter-of-factly, hoping the need to answer would calm her. "When did you last see Bess?"

Mrs. Zimmer swallowed. "Saturday morning. She had breakfast with us, with Harry and me. It's a family thing. We always have breakfast together on the weekend."

"And then?"

"She said she was going to the beach."

"Didn't you expect her for dinner?"

"Yes."

She had been hesitant, Norah thought. "Had Bess stayed away all night on any other occasion?"

A deep sigh and then Mrs. Zimmer bowed her head. "Yes."

"Often?"

"Once or twice. Harry didn't know. I didn't want him to know. I'd tell him to go to bed and I'd wait up for her. He goes to work at five-thirty in the morning. He needs his sleep."

"And when she finally came home on these occasions, was she all right?"

"No. Oh, God, no." Again there was the danger of losing control, but Yolanda Zimmer managed to hang on. "She was in bad shape. I couldn't hide that from Harry. We were just crazy over it. We didn't know what to do. And then all of a sudden, she stopped. She stopped using. It was all over. We didn't know why or how it happened; we were afraid to ask. We just thanked the dear Lord for His mercy. We thought she was cured. We did. So we left it alone. Harry wanted her to get a summer job, said it would keep her out of trouble, but I said no—she's still young, let her enjoy herself. Time enough for the hardships of life. Let her enjoy her youth. Let her have her fun." The tears came again, but quietly.

Norah jumped in before it could get worse. "Who is Stanley Belkin?"

"He's the boy she's going with . . . was going with currently. She has . . . had . . . so many. She was so pretty, full of pep, popular. All the boys were after her. You have no idea."

"Do you know Stanley?"

"Yes. He's a good kid. Clean. I believe he's clean. He heads up a small rock band. They play at school dances. Bess sings . . . used to sing . . . with them sometimes. He's all right."

"When Bess didn't come home Saturday night, did you check with Stanley?"

"Of course. He hadn't seen her all day."

"What did you do then?"

"I called her other friends, but nobody had seen her."

"Had she been to the beach?"

Mrs. Zimmer looked away. "No."

That was when she should have told her husband. That was when the two of them should have called the police. Though in different economic circumstances, she and Mrs. Hurlock were essentially the same. Each had been hungry for her only child's love. Each had tried to buy it with permissiveness, by shielding the girl from her father's discipline. The price had been higher than they could have imagined.

Sighing, Norah looked to Reissig, who indicated he had no other questions. "If anything else occurs to you, Mrs. Zimmer, or if you need anything, you can reach either one of us at . . ." she pulled a card from her wallet and was about to hand it over.

"Where is she?" Mrs. Zimmer demanded. "Where's Bess? I want to see her."

A formal identification of the body would have to be made, but the woman was in no condition for the ordeal. Who ever was? Again, Norah silently consulted Gary.

"Perhaps you should wait till your husband gets home, Ma'am. He's been notified and is on his way."

"I don't want to wait. I want to see her now. I want to be with her."

That was not possible yet. She would be denied that consolation for many days, Norah thought. Mrs. Zimmer would be shown her daughter's body on a slab. Norah didn't know what the facilities were at the Nassau County morgue, but surely she would be separated from actual contact. She would have to accept the further insult to her child of the autopsy. Then, only then, the patched-up remains would be delivered to a funeral home and, at last, she could be with her for a few hours before interment.

Norah took a very deep breath. "We'll drive you over."

*   *   *

Stanley Belkin presented himself voluntarily at the station house in Far Rockaway the next morning just as Gary Reissig and Norah were on their way out to look for him.

He was a tall, muscular but slightly overweight young man of seventeen or eighteen, bursting with health and all the privileges his parents' money could buy.

"The FBI came over to my house last night—about my van."

He was bewildered by the situation he found himself embroiled in, confused, as though he had a special dispensation from sorrow or disaster or pain as his birthright. "I figured you'd want to talk to me too." His expression indicated he had come to save them all trouble because he had had no part in anything that happened.

"Thanks for coming in." Reissig waved him to a chair. "About the van—did you give Bess Zimmer permission to use it."

"No. She just took it."

"She ever drive it before?"

"Oh, sure. Lots of times. She was a good driver. Her dad wouldn't let her have wheels of her own so when she wanted to go shopping or something like that—if we didn't have a gig, the group, you know—I let her take it."

"She always asked permission?"

"Yeah. Right." He bobbed his head.

"Until Saturday."

"Yeah."

"When did you notice the van was gone?"

"After her mother called Saturday night. I went out to the garage to get it thinking I'd go look for her."

"You had an idea where she might be."

"No. I just thought I'd drive around."

"Drive around where?"

The youth shrugged. "Around."

"When you discovered your van was gone why did you assume Bess had taken it?" Norah wanted to know.

"I just . . . she was the only one who drove it besides me."

"You must have had some notion of why she'd wanted it. Where she'd be going."

He bit his lip. "There were a couple of places I thought of looking."

"Such as?"

"She wasn't there."

"So you did go after her?"

"Yes, Ma'am. My dad let me use his car."

"Where did you go?"

Stanley appealed to the man. "Do I have to say?"

"You want to help, don't you? Isn't that why you came?"

"Jeez . . ." Belkin wiped his face with an open palm. He had come to get himself off the hook and Reissig's steady stare made him ashamed. "Okay. A couple of kids at school deal. Bess was doing coke for a while. A lot of the kids are, a lot. But Bess stopped. For one thing, she couldn't afford it. For another, she got picked up and spent a night in jail. Her mother went down and got her out, but she was scared for her dad to know; he would have beat her. She was clean for close to a year. Then she started again. Naturally, she denied it, but I could tell. I did see her on Saturday. She came to the beach but she didn't stick around. She was hurting. I didn't tell her mother because I figured that would only make her more frantic. I figured Bess was going for a fix and I could find her. But she wasn't anywhere I looked."

"She might have been and gone," Norah suggested.

Stanley clenched his teeth.

"You don't want to snitch on your friends, is that it?"

Belkin hung his head. Though he had reached his full physical development, emotionally he was still adolescent.

"You consider them friends?"

He flushed under his tan. "Neither of them would have hurt Bess."

"Killed her you mean. Are you sure?"

"If she'd OD'd on some bad stuff, that's one thing, but they told me she was stabbed."

"It wasn't one, neat surgical incision, you know," Norah told him. "Her throat was sliced through. Her head was

almost separated from her neck. Maybe you ought to come
to the morgue and look at her."

His face went from scarlet to gray. "They wouldn't do
that, neither one of them. Not Jay or Pete. They wouldn't."

"Jay and Pete who?"

He groaned, then made up his mind. "Jason Tate and Pete
Hayman. Between them they supply the whole school. I
don't mean that *all* the kids are using. I mean . . . oh, hell!"
He mustered enough courage to make a countercharge.
"They don't give the stuff away, you know."

"At least we got two names out of him," Reissig observed
after Belkin left.

"Do you believe either one of those two high school kids
murdered four women and engineered a $12 million heist?"

"It's back down to $8 million."

"Whatever."

Reissig sighed. "No, of course I don't. But we've got to
talk to them. One of them might know something, especially
if he was supplying the girl."

"Like where she got the money to pay for the junk."
Norah echoed Stanley Belkin's parting shot.

Norah and Gary split up to interrogate each boy individually. Their stories were predictably similar. Both Pete Hayman and Jason Tate were frightened: of their parents finding
out what they were up to; of what their mob connection
would do to them if they informed; but most of all they were
scared of being suspected of having killed Bess Zimmer. At
the start, each denied any drug dealing, any involvement
with her habit. They didn't dare deny knowing the girl, that
would have been too easy to disprove. But once having been
led to admit their drug activities each insisted it was all in the
past. Finished. Over with. It had ended with the school year
and each swore he had no intention of resuming in the fall.
As though drug addiction were a seasonal thing. *Believe me,
sir or ma'am, if Bess was getting it, she wasn't getting it from
me.* The protestations were identical. *Maybe some of the
other kids might know. Why don't you ask around?*

Of course, they did. What they got were the names of three more teenage dealers and a long list of young customers, terrifyingly young, reaching down into grade school. They turned all the information over to the Nassau Narcotics Squad.

At the end of the week, Norah and Gary met for lunch. They didn't go to his home, not because Norah didn't like it, rather she liked it too much. The children, in spite of their handicaps—or maybe because of them—were loving and cheerful and as undemanding as puppies. Millicent Crouse showed no resentment of Norah on her daughter's behalf, yet Norah was reluctant to go back. She told herself she would not be able to focus her full attention on business. So Gary took her instead to a small waterside café on the other side of the channel. The sun was bright, the breeze cool. The Rockaway beaches were dotted with sunbathers and colorful unbrellas. A dog ran barking happily along the water's edge. Gary ordered beers and they came in frosted glasses. Norah took it all in, savored it, and then dismissed it.

"I think Bess Zimmer had a very special connection, a connection all her own that none of the other kids had any idea about."

"The killer?"

"Right."

The FBI had had time to examine the van abandoned on the shoulder of the parkway from which Bess had tried to escape. They had turned up torn pieces of bills which proved to be part of the Federal Reserve shipment held over the weekend at Mercury, as well as shreds of canvas of the kind used in the manufacture of the money sacks. It was generally accepted that the van had been used in the heist.

"Not knowing how to drive is no big handicap in the city," Norah reasoned aloud. "But out here, it's another thing. Besides, it was vital in pulling off the job. The other women supplied the perpetrator with information. When he got what he needed to know from each one, he killed her. But Bess was his 'wheel man.' She was the only one who participated in the commission of the robbery. She couldn't be silenced beforehand. He was helpless without her. So he made sure of her silence in the only way he could—by supplying her habit."

"I'll buy it." But Gary wasn't happy. Instead of narrowing the field, Norah's reasoning had just extended its scope.

Norah sighed because she knew it.

Captain Jacoby took an uncharacteristically optimistic view. He called Norah into his office for a rare word of commendation.

"I want you to keep on it," he told her. He even smiled. "If you need additional help, just ask."

Additional! Norah thought. So far, except for Gary, who was operating out of another command and putting in a lot of his own time, she was working alone. Of course, the FBI and Bank Robbery Squad were tailing Dobriansky, Hurlock, and the employees of both Mercury Courier Service and Thor Security. They must have had at least fifty men deployed, but they were concerned primarily with recovering the money. She wanted the killer.

"Yes, Captain, I will. Thank you," Norah settled for the good will, for as long as it might last.

Four women, she thought as she returned to her desk, sat and slid low to stretch her legs underneath. The big, crowded room was noisy and hot, but it was still a relief after Jacoby's sauna. Norah shifted her chair to get into the airflow from the nearest fan. Four different and disparate personalities, but each had had useful information to impart— and in Bess's case a function to perform. Since they were not haphazardly chosen victims, not victims of opportunity attacked and butchered out of a passion to kill, then by what means had he selected them? It began with Nancy Hurlock, a bank teller. Had he been searching for a crime to commit? Had he been thinking about a bank job and made her acquaintance with the purpose of getting information about the bank only to discover a much bigger prize? Learning that Nancy's father was an executive of the Mercury Courier Service and that she had worked there herself for a time, had he set his sights higher? Had Nancy finally suspected? Was that why he had had to get rid of her before the robbery? That would have necessitated his seeking other sources for the things he still needed to know. It would have also set the pattern for killing those other sources—in advance.

Norah felt her excitement mount. Nancy Hurlock had worked in Manhattan, but the warehouse he wanted to hit was out on Long Island. So that was why he went there to look for the women who could tell him what he still needed to know. With the exception of Nancy's, all the murders were committed within a ten-square-mile area! May Guttman—she had provided the delivery schedule—had worked at a diner catering to truck drivers. She heard them talking; she passed on what she heard. She couldn't tell him about the alarm system though. The third victim, Lila Cestone, had not worked for Thor Security, however.

Norah gritted her teeth, worked her lips back and forth. Lila had worked for the J.C. Marshall Company. No good. Was it possible that Lila had worked for Thor in the past? But how could he have known that? She shook her head. It didn't work. She was on the wrong track. Yet she was reluctant to give up the theory. If only she had someone to talk it out with. If only Joe were here. She sighed, then smiled ruefully. She knew exactly what Joe would have said: *You don't solve cases sitting on your duff in the squad room.*

Thor headquarters was situated on Sunrise Highway in Valley Stream in a squat, suburban-style office building of red brick surrounded by lawn and a few unimaginatively placed shrubs. To one accustomed to high-rises on minuscule city plots, it seemed to sprawl horizontally, prodigal of space, but out here space was cheap, Norah thought. She was surprised that the actual size of the security system's offices was so small. The decor was limited to the necessities, with floor tile rather than carpet, flat lighting, bare walls. In the cubicle serving as the reception area, a surprisingly stylish young woman with frizzled brown hair sat at an ordinary electric typewriter. Her fingers flew over the keyboard. To her right was a small telephone console. At a ring, she picked up and continued typing while she listened. Impressive. The name plate on her desk said: Mara Lynn Hoffritz. She stopped typing just long enough to switch the call and replace the receiver.

Norah introduced herself.

Mara Lynn's perfectly arched eyebrows didn't have far up to go. "If it's about the robbery, Sergeant, I don't know what I can tell you that I haven't told all the others—over and over."

Attractive, efficient, self-assured, but no more so than May Guttman or Lila Cestone, Norah thought. Why had he passed her by?

"That's what I'm here to find out."

Mara Lynn waved a beautifully manicured hand to include the typewriter and papers on her desk. "I've got so much work . . ."

How had she escaped?

"If you'd like to talk to our head of operations, Mr. Sachs? He's not in just now, but I can set up an appointment."

"I'm not primarily interested in the robbery. I'm investigating the murders."

"Murders?"

"I'm interested in the robbery only as it involves the murders of four young women. I'm looking for the 'slasher.'"

That was what the media had dubbed the murderer and it was apparent the slick and efficient receptionist was well acquainted with the case. She had read about it and probably seen the grisly depictions on television.

"The latest victim was the girl who drove the van for the robber. Do you drive a car, Ms. Hoffritz?"

She nodded, her dark eyes very wide and frightened. "I don't know anything about any of this."

"You may have met the killer."

"Me?"

"I want you to think back over the past two months." There was no use asking if she had given information about the workings of Thor Security to anyone; she would instinctively deny it and her instincts would be true—if the slasher had got what he wanted from Mara Lynn, he wouldn't have needed to go on to Lila Cestone. "Have you dated anybody new recently? Maybe only once or twice."

"No."

"I suppose you meet a number of men during the course of your work day—salesmen, suppliers, people coming in to buy your systems; to enquire about them?"

"Not that many. We don't buy anything much beyond office supplies and those are ordered by mail or telephone. Sometimes I just go to the shopping center if we run short." By a movement of her head she indicated the general direction of the small mall Norah had noticed perhaps a quarter of a mile down. "As for clients, we have a sales force that goes out and calls on them."

"No one has come in recently to enquire about Thor Alarm Systems?"

"No."

There was one last possibility. "How about new employees? Has anyone been fired or quit recently?"

"No. We haven't hired anybody new for . . ." she stopped. A shadow of uncertainty passed over her perfect face. "Somebody did come in to enquire about work. About . . . say, three weeks or a month ago. I told him even if we had an opening all our people were either ex–police officers or had a lot of experience with private security. We make a thorough check into the applicant's background. I told him if he had that kind of qualification there was plenty of work available and he shouldn't have any trouble finding a job."

"And that was the end of it?"

"Yes."

"Are you sure?"

"Well," she shrugged. "He wanted to take me out to lunch." She smiled. "He said he appreciated my taking the time and trouble to explain and he wanted to take me to lunch."

"And did you go?"

"I couldn't. I had another date—with my husband."

Norah grinned. "Did you tell him that?"

"After he asked me to break the date." She grinned back.

So then he'd had to go and look for someone else, Norah thought. "Do you remember what he looked like?"

"He was attractive all right. Dark hair and dark eyes. He came on real sexy. I guess if I weren't married and in love with my husband, I probably would have gone out with him." She shuddered. "Is he the one, do you think?"

"Would you know him if you saw him again?"

Mara Lynn hesitated. The initial fear had been instinctive and vague. Now that it was focused on a specific person, it was gripping. "I don't think so."

Trying to reassure a nervous witness was a familiar problem, there was no set procedure. "Do you think you remember him well enough to help a police artist draw a likeness?"

"No. I really don't remember him at all. I'm sorry." The receptionist closed her mouth, clamped it shut as though she never intended to open it again.

"Your identity would remain anonymous, of course," Norah told her but it didn't help. "You said he was dark and good-looking. How tall was he? Thin or fat? How old?"

Mara Lynn shook her head obdurately. In the end, unless she could make a positive ID, it didn't really matter, Norah consoled herself. Descriptions by untrained observers were notoriously unreliable. Ten different witnesses gave ten different descriptions. What one dubbed young, another thought middle-aged. Cases of mistaken identity abounded. Yet every instinct pulsed with the conviction that Mara Lynn had gotten a good and unemotional look at the killer. She would be accurate. But she was scared, and she had more reason than the others.

"I could arrange protection for you, Mrs. Hoffritz, but that would call his attention to you and apparently up to now he hasn't considered you a threat." Norah didn't like using this particular technique, but she was convinced it was necessary. "Actually, I think if you make sure your husband is with you at home at all times and don't pick up strangers while driving, there's nothing to be afraid of."

"Oh, God!"

"Meantime, if you should happen to think of something, anything . . ." Norah handed her her card.

"I told him the best bet was to get a job in a department store or maybe as a guard in an office. Practically all the companies have them nowadays. I told him to try J. C. Marshall down the road. They're clients of ours." She was desperate to pass on responsibility.

Which was exactly what she had done at the time.

Reissig met Norah at Lila Cestone's place.

The garden duplex remained intact pending inventory by the executor of the estate. His first action on unlocking the door was to walk over to the air conditioner and flip the switch. Nothing. He tried the lights. No juice.

"Lilco doesn't waste time turning off service," he commented wryly. "A while back one of my gas bills went astray. I didn't notice. So, I was working and the phone rang around six. It was Millicent screaming she had gone to the stove to cook dinner and there was no gas. The service men had come while she was at the market and without a word to anyone just turned it off at the street."

It was nearly seven; in another month it would be dark at this hour but for now it was still daylight. Norah felt a sudden twinge of sadness that another summer was nearly over. It had been an empty summer for her, lonely, and the work hadn't engrossed her as in the past. Maybe now that Joe was gone, and her father, she demanded too much? She looked around. The room was of medium size but nicely proportioned, with a fireplace on one wall and bookshelves flanking it. Certain of the shelves were used to display a collection of china—birds, possibly Spode, and shepherdesses—Dresden? That meant money. On the mantel was a row of silver and brass trophies. For what? She went over to see and picked up a goblet. It couldn't be gold. It was decorated with jewels—amethysts and rubies. They couldn't be real.

Chapter ——————
—————— FIFTEEN

A small cross was engraved on the base of the chalice. Norah could hardly contain her excitement.

"I think I know where this came from. It was stolen from the church of Our Lady of Perpetual Help about . . . well, actually the Monday morning after Nancy Hurlock's murder. On July twenty-second, the thief was still trying to dispose of it." She handed Gary the photograph Father Boylan had given her.

"Sure looks like it. You think he sold it to Lila?"

"He needed money to supply Bess Zimmer's habit. I think this is how he got it."

"I don't know . . ."

"Lila Cestone was, let's say, smitten with her new boyfriend, but she wasn't a complete fool. He was, from every indication, of a lower class than she, not well educated, and—we know—out of work. She wouldn't be likely to give him any money, not in any large amount anyway. Maybe he showed her the chalice, claimed it was an heirloom, belonged to his mother or something like that, and offered it as security for a loan."

"Would she go for that?"

"She probably had doubts, but she was in love and she didn't want to lose him."

"He must have been some kind of ladykiller," Reissig said.

Norah took a deep breath and released it slowly. "You could call him that." She went over to the desk. "Let's hope she paid him by check."

The canceled checks for the month of July had not yet been returned, but the checkbook was there in the middle drawer, and Norah and Reissig went through it together. All payments were neatly listed. In the case of a payment to a department store, the merchandise was itemized: Plymouth Shop—two blouses; Sear's—steam iron and ironing board. Norah's heart jumped when she saw the entry marked simply—cash. The check was in the amount of fifteen hundred dollars.

"This has to be it. He had to endorse it. All we have to do is go to the bank."

"Unless she cashed it herself and handed him the money."

"Why be negative?"

"Because he hasn't made a single mistake up to now," Gary retorted. "I don't think he made this one."

"He's shrewd and he's devious, but he's no genius?" Norah flared. "Why should he anticipate that anybody would be examining Lila Cestone's canceled checks? He needed the money and he wouldn't want to arouse his lady friend's suspicions by refusing a check."

"Okay, okay. We'll go to the bank."

"I'm sorry. I didn't mean to be irritable, but there's something here that's eluding me. I can't put my finger on it."

"You shouldn't let yourself get emotionally involved."

She stared at him. "That's what my husband used to tell me."

"It's a lesson we all have to learn."

"I know, but this case is special. Four young women have been killed absolutely in cold blood. And it isn't just that— they were courted first, their loneliness exploited till their guard was down. Then they were slaughtered like animals. It's not just the brutality of it. I have a sense about the killer, he's . . ."

"Not responsible? Insane?"

"No, I don't believe that. I never did. There's too much

planning and scheming. I feel that although he used these women and then killed them without mercy, he is capable of deep feeling, maybe even of an obsessive emotion. That he's being driven."

"Well, we'll know more when we get to the bank in the morning. I'll pick you up at your place for breakfast. Seven okay?"

"I don't want to put you to the trouble of driving all the way into the city and then back out here again."

"No trouble."

That night at home Norah set herself to all the housekeeping chores she'd been neglecting recently. She didn't allow herself to speculate on the odds that Lila Cestone's check had been endorsed by the killer. She thought instead about Gary Reissig. In many ways he was like Joe, but also very different. He was steady and supportive. He was a good, though perhaps plodding, cop. He loved his family—the two handicapped children. Where Joe had been outgoing, very sociable, Gary was more of a loner. As she was. He loved the outdoors—fishing, swimming, skin-diving, basically noncompetitive sports. She felt at ease with him, but she would never let herself get seriously involved with another cop. Never.

She thought of Adrian Gourdine. He was everything the other two were not. He was sophisticated. Joe had been sophisticated but in a different, almost innocent way. Gourdine was self-focused, ego-oriented. That made Norah think of the killer. Gourdine used women, but he would not kill. Was that because he lacked the courage or the core of the obsession?

Norah worked till she was bone weary. When she turned out the lights, she fell asleep right away.

The next morning, Gary picked her up as agreed. They had a silent but companionable breakfast. They had reached the stage, Norah mused, of old friends who share their thoughts instinctively, without words, in a very short time. A condition she would not achieve with Gourdine no matter how long they might know each other, or how intimately. In fact, Norah thought, the longer the association with Gourdine lasted, the more superficial and tempestuous it would become.

Gary paid their check and they left. At that hour traffic was light leaving the city, so they reached Lila's branch of the Peninsula Bank shortly after it opened its doors. The check for fifteen hundred dollars made out to cash had been endorsed by the recipient. Unfortunately, it had also been cashed there, so there was no clue as to where the killer might be living. But that was only passing disappointment. What mattered was the name. Frank Salgo.

It struck an instant chord. He had been a pupil of Sister Therese, one of the three that moved out of the neighborhood without a trace. Father Boylan's reasoning that no stranger had wandered into the church and stolen the chalice was impeccable, Norah thought. How much more of his theory was valid, she wasn't ready to consider. First, she had to find Salgo.

If it was young Frank Salgo who had not only stolen the chalice but also broken into the poorbox on that earlier occasion, Norah reasoned, then it might not be the first time he had stolen. On that assumption, she went down to the Juvenile Bureau on Lafayette Street. She got nowhere. The people she talked to refused to tell her if Frank Salgo even had a record, much less allow her a look at it. It wasn't her first encounter with the Juvenile Justice System, so she wasn't surprised—disappointed, disgusted, frustrated, but not surprised. One of the candidates for governor in the last campaign had made a suggestion regarding the handling of child criminals. His idea: the criminal record of the juvenile offender should be opened to police, judges, social workers, prosecutors, and defenders. If, after the first arrest, the child committed no further crimes, then at age twenty-one the record would be sealed. He would begin adult life without blemish. Meanwhile, the trials for children accused of violent crimes and felonies would be held in a special branch of adult court, the Family Court remaining, as was originally intended, a place for settling matters of runaways and child abuse—to shelter and cherish the children before they became criminal.

That eminently sensible and compassionate proposal had been swept away with the campaign literature. Those who cared about the children and about real justice were stymied by the rigid rule of silence.

Norah's next move was an appeal to the administrative judge.

Judge Tully received Sergeant Mulcahaney in chambers. Norah presented herself at the end of the afternoon session. The meeting was supposed to be informal.

Judge Tully was in her early fifties, but certainly didn't look it. She had a pink-and-white complexion with few lines to mar its freshness. Her hair, blonde and styled in the manner of her youth, called a "pageboy" then, had only the merest shading of silver at the center of her brow. It was as though a ray of sun highlighted that particular strand. Her eyes were a clear gray, bulging slightly. She wore a gray tailored suit. She looked bland, but Norah knew better. She knew Judge Martha Tully's reputation. Martha Tully had argued as a lawyer to the letter of the law. Norah had read reports and articles about her. She took note that the office was heavily air conditioned so the judge could keep her suit jacket on comfortably. That was a further clue to the judge's nature and to what was coming.

Having waved Sergeant Mulcahaney to a chair, Judge Tully glanced at the paper in front of her.

"Ordinarily, I would deny this request without discussion, Sergeant, but your chief of detectives called and asked that I grant you this interview."

Well! Norah thought, good for Manny Jacoby. She had gone to the captain before making formal application and apparently he had gone right up the chain of command to get her the backing they had both sensed—no, feared—she would need.

"Thank you, Your Honor."

"In your request to have the records opened of one Frank Salgo, you cite *probable cause*. You cite the theft of a chalice from Our Lady of Perpetual Help church and connect it with the previous theft of money from the poorbox from that same church, and the murder of one of the nuns in the convent. In my opinion, even if Frank Salgo did, in fact, steal the chalice, there is no basis whatsoever for your assumption that he committed the earlier misdemeanor. To attempt to link him to a homicide is completely unacceptable."

"Your Honor, all I'm asking—"

"I have studied your background, Sergeant," Judge Tully continued inexorably. "I am aware of the traumatic events in your life on the night Sister Therese was killed. Inevitably they must color your judgment."

Norah gasped.

"You have my sympathy, but unless you can offer real evidence to tie Frank Salgo to the earlier theft, I cannot allow the record to be opened to you."

Norah's blue eyes darkened. She pulled herself very straight, chin thrust out. "I didn't come here for sympathy, Your Honor. Also, I bitterly resent the implication that I'm conducting a personal vendetta."

"You must learn to be precise, Sergeant," Judge Tully was patronizing and soothing at the same time. "What I said was this—you were influenced by the fact that your husband was killed on the same night and, in fact, while you were investigating the nun's murder. That homicide is still unsolved and the need to clear it must be considered a motivating force."

"Are you a psychiatrist, Your Honor?"

Martha Tully's pink-and-white face tightened. The gray eyes flashed. "You're being insolent, Sergeant."

"I apologize, but if you have the right to interpret my actions, then you must permit me to draw certain conclusions about Frank Salgo. He was one of the three students of Sister Therese whom the police were not able to locate after the theft and murder. Now his name turns up again in connection with another robbery at the church.

This, in turn, is linked with the Mercury warehouse robbery and four brutal stabbings. I can't ignore it. I just want to locate Frank Salgo and talk to him. I don't even want to see his juvenile record. What I'm concerned with is beyond juvenile crime." She took a breath. "If you'll read my request, Your Honor, you'll note all I want is his most recent address."

Martha Tully's lips set into a tight line as she glanced down at the papers in front of her. Apparently, she had skimmed over the exact wording and taken it for granted that this was the usual plea to open the files. She was not pleased at her own carelessness.

She looked directly at Norah. "That's all?"

In the past the judge had been taken to task by the media for some of her decisions. She had been criticized both for leniency and for strictness. In every instance, Judge Tully had toughed it out. Norah knew even a suggestion that she might, by denying this request, be subjected again to public opprobrium would only harden her resistance. To remind her of the brutality of the crimes wouldn't help either.

"That's all, Your Honor."

Martha Tully's eyes neither wavered nor softened, but suddenly she bent her head, took a pen, and quickly, firmly signed the paper. She thrust it at Norah.

"It's a matter of doing the job, Sergeant."

Norah took the paper and folded it. "It's a matter of serving justice, Your Honor."

That was an argument it would take more than a few words to resolve.

Frank Salgo's mother had remarried. The police had not known and had not sought her under her new name, Magda Petrus. Having been instructed only to give the address, the social worker was careful not to reveal anything more. All Norah learned was confirmation of what she had suspected—a complaint (Juvenile Justice jargon) had been lodged against Frank Salgo. She had no idea of its nature or of the judge's finding and subsequent disposition (Juvenile

Justice euphemism for sentencing). It would have helped to know, but she didn't waste time or effort trying to coax it out. Instead, Norah went down to the street, got into her Honda, and drove out to Sunnyside.

She parked under the El at a meter directly opposite the address she had been given. It turned out to be a four-story, yellow brick building with a bar and grill on the street and apartments above. Norah got out, locked her car, and crossed Queens Boulevard. She strolled casually by the plate glass window of Homer's and looked inside. It was just after five and the place was nearly full. It was your ordinary neighborhood tavern crowded with the locals—men in shirtsleeves, their creased faces glistening with the sweat of conviviality. One or two young couples occupied booths; otherwise everybody stood at the bar. Tucked to the side was the entrance, one door for the bar and another leading to the apartments. Norah searched and found the name of Petrus immediately. She rang.

"Yes?" A woman's voice answered.

"Mrs. Petrus? Police. May I come up, please?"

"Police?"

"Sergeant Mulcahaney, Twentieth Precinct, Mrs. Petrus. You can call and check it out."

"What do you want?"

"I'd like to talk to you, Mrs. Petrus. If you prefer, you can come downstairs."

"No. I guess it's all right."

Nevertheless there was a considerable wait before the buzzer sounded and the lock released. Norah entered a hallway facing stairs. There was no elevator; there wasn't room for one. It only meant climbing one flight anyway. When she got to the landing, Norah saw the door of 2A was ajar but on a chain.

"Sergeant Mulcahaney? Do you have identification?"

"Of course." Norah showed it to her.

Grudgingly, she was admitted.

The room was small, shabby, but colorful. It was an eclectic confusion of good oriental rugs, much worn, bright pillows in hot pink, orange, and purple, fringed silk lampshades, and cheap bric-a-brac. None of it clean. Magda Petrus wore a luxurious but stained satin robe and high-heeled slippers. Huge golden half-moon earrings dangled and pulled at her earlobes. A chunky pseudo-antique medallion hung on a heavy gold chain around her neck. The jewelry was too ostentatious to be anything but costume stuff. Her long black hair was loose and streaming down her back. Her eyes were teary and her red nose confirmed a summer cold. At her best, Norah thought, she probably wasn't much of a housekeeper. Unkempt in her own person, even slatternly, the woman exuded a high degree of sensuality. She was full-bodied, her features were thick, but her skin was smooth, her dark eyes large, her hair an abundant glory. There was no easy way to lead into what she had to say, Norah thought.

"It's about your son, Mrs. Petrus. He's the one I'm looking for. Frank Salgo."

"Why? What do you want with Frank?"

She was guarded but not anxious.

"I've been looking for Frank for some time, ever since you moved away from Manhattan."

"That was over two years ago."

"Is that when you remarried?"

"Yes. What do you want with Frank?"

Anxiety now curled at the edges of her composure.

"Where is he? I'd like to talk to him."

"I don't know where he is. He doesn't live with us anymore."

"Oh?"

"He and Homer, my husband, didn't get along. Frank was at that age when boys don't know what to do with themselves. They don't know what they want out of life. They resent adults; they resent being told what to do. Finally, Frank just walked out."

"How long since he left?"

"Maybe . . . four months."

"And you don't know where he went? You haven't seen or heard from him?"

Magda Petrus frowned and pursed her lips.

"For nearly two years your husband and your son managed somehow to get along, then suddenly four months ago your boy left home. Why? What happened?"

"He wasn't with us two years. He was away in that place in the Bronx. He was there when we got married. He only got out this past February. You must know that. Why are you pretending you don't?"

Norah caught her breath. That place in the Bronx must be Spofford, the juvenile facility for violent offenders.

"So he was only with you a couple of months. What happened?"

Magda Petrus considered a long time. Then she sighed. "They had a fight, Homer and Frank. Frank didn't want to work downstairs. He couldn't hold any other job. He just lay around all day and stayed out all night. Homer wouldn't put up with it. He told him either to get a job or get out. Frank pulled a knife on him."

"Did he cut him?"

There was the slightest of pauses. "It didn't amount to anything."

Norah didn't believe it, but she didn't challenge it. The woman was holding back—maybe just the extent of her husband's injuries that night or maybe a lot more. "Could you give me the names of Frank's friends? Maybe one of them might know where to reach him."

"I don't know any of his friends."

"How about girlfriends? Is Frank popular with the girls?"

"He always said I was his best girl."

Why did mothers preen themselves about that? Norah wondered. She said nothing. Silence was often the best goad.

"You still haven't told me why you want him."

Not this time, Norah thought and sighed. "Frank stole a

valuable chalice from the altar of Our Lady of Perpetual Help. That was your old parish, wasn't it?"

"He stole from the church?"

Though she showed dismay, Norah had a feeling she was relieved.

"He took a precious vessel from the altar?" Magda Petrus went over and sat so that she was partially sideways, away from Norah.

"He sold it to a woman named Lila Cestone. Maybe you've heard of her?"

"No."

"She was stabbed to death July twenty-ninth. Maybe you remember. You must have read about it. She was the third victim in a series of brutal slashings. Each woman was killed in or near her car."

"Oh, my God," Magda Petrus murmured and the color rose, suffusing her broad face, making her look five years younger.

"We have the check made out and signed by her, and endorsed by him. The chalice was in her home."

Magda Petrus frowned. "Maybe Frank did take the chalice. Maybe he did rob the poorbox, but he didn't kill anybody."

The theft from the poorbox had not been mentioned in the papers or on television in connection with the case. Norah was very careful not to show her excitement. "But he did know Miss Cestone and so he might be able to help us."

"Frank's not a bad boy. Children steal, lots of them do. It isn't even stealing, it's more . . . they just take . . . something they want. They don't realize they shouldn't."

"Somebody has to teach them."

"Yes. I did my best for him. I did everything I could. It wasn't easy, either. The point is he got into trouble, but he paid for it, and now it's over and done with. Are you going to hound him for it for the rest of his life?"

"I don't know anything about Frank's past offenses, Mrs. Petrus."

"I'll bet."

Norah didn't bother to argue. "Does Frank drive?"

Magda Petrus hesitated. "Why should I tell you any-thing." She fumbled in the pocket of her soiled dressing gown, brought out a balled-up Kleenex and managed to find a corner to blow her nose and wipe her eyes. "The boy never had a decent break, Sergeant. His father, Stefan, was a vio-lent man, a drunken brawler who finished a night's carousing by coming home and beating up on me. When Frank, little as he was, tried to defend me, he ended up getting licked himself. Finally, Stefan walked out on both of us. I did my best, but I wasn't brought up to work. The only job I could get was cleaning other women's houses. It was barely enough for us to live on. Frank saw what the other kids had and since I couldn't provide it, he learned to take what he wanted. He learned how to snatch from the younger ones, the little ones. He grabbed a portable radio from a school-mate. The child held on and was shoved back and fell. His head hit the cement and he died. It was an accident."

And not the cause of his having been sent to Spofford, apparently.

"It brought Frank to the attention of a recruiter for the Scorcese family," Mrs. Petrus went on.

Now they were getting to it, Norah thought. Not that it was anything new. It had become common practice for crime bosses to use children to run numbers, collect money—teen-age bagmen. The police were well aware of it, but what could they do? When they picked up such a child, he had to be turned over to Family Court. The sentence was always minimal and often the young offender was simply returned home on probation to go right back to work. It was a Fagin situation Charles Dickens could not even have imagined.

"Frank turned out to be reliable enough and clever enough to be promoted to running drugs. He brought home his take. He was proud. He put his first five hundred dollars in front of me and I slapped him." Magda Petrus put work-coarsened hands with brightly lacquered nails up to her face.

"From then on I lost all control of him," she continued. "He did what he wanted and he had plenty of money to do it with. Till he got caught. Then they sent him away to that place. When he got out his job wasn't there anymore. He was too old."

And spoiled for ordinary work, Norah thought. Washed up at sixteen. Was it possible that Frank Salgo had applied to the Scorcese family once more? That he had submitted his idea for the heist along with information about the vulnerability of the Mercury warehouse that he had got from Nancy? On that basis, he would surely had been hired back, Norah thought. It fitted. It made sense.

"It's your fault, you, the police!" his mother lashed out. "If you had dealt with Frank at the beginning, when he was twelve and his friend died, if you had punished him then . . . But you let him get away with it. You let him work three years for the syndicate without touching him! What did you expect him to turn into?"

There were answers Norah could have made, explanations she could have given, but no defense.

Her silence at last fired Magda Petrus. "So you go find him! You deal with him. He's your responsibility!" she shouted and sank from anger into sobbing despair.

Chapter SIXTEEN

Norah stayed till Magda Petrus calmed down. When asked for a photograph of Frank, all Magda could offer were snapshots dating back to when he attended the parochial school. Rather than apply again to Judge Tully for access to Salgo's file, Norah asked Mrs. Petrus to work with a police artist to create a more recent likeness. Resistance burned out, Mrs. Petrus agreed.

Any doubts Norah had about how honest the rendering would be were erased when she saw the finished portrait. It matched the bits of description she'd been able to cull. The face long and thin, forehead high with dark, wavy hair sweeping back from a peak. The eyes dark and brooding, the lips sensuous, the nose long and straight. Frank Salgo was strikingly good-looking and if, as Magda Petrus claimed, he had little interest in girls, girls would certainly take an interest in him. He bore little resemblance to his mother, Norah noted. She was short and her body compact. Her hair, also dark, was coarse and her skin, though without blemish, swarthy. He must take after his father.

Where before Norah hadn't been able to get even a full description of the suspect, now she had a portrait. With high hopes, she set out to show the drawing to the friends and neighbors of the victims. The disappointment was deep when no one recognized him. No one remembered having seen him.

It was ten days since the discovery of the body of Bess
Zimmer. With the last days of August the weather changed;
the terrible heat lifted and the emotional climate of the city
cooled. The young women, particularly those dependent on
their cars, were reassured. Even the media found other
more recent horrors to exploit. Norah had a rare weekend
off coming to her and she decided to take a real break.
Adrian Gourdine chose that time to call and invite her to the
opening of an exhibition of Rennaissance art at the Metropolitan and then dinner. Gary Reissig, knowing her schedule, called too. Summer was ending, he said. While the
weather held, would she come out to the house? This was
the best time of year at the shore.

Norah knew which invitation she *should* accept and which
one she would. She liked Gary very much; he was a competent officer, a good companion. She respected and sympathized with his personal problem; her heart went out to his
two handicapped children. But Toni's art teacher stirred and
challenged her. She expected he would pressure her to go to
bed with him. She wasn't sure she could resist. She wasn't
sure she wanted to resist. *I'm not a young girl anymore,* she
thought. *I'm a widow. Does it make sense to maintain the
same moral code I had before I was married?*

She called Gary intending to say she had to work after all,
but she liked him too much to deceive him. So she told him
she had already made other plans. That made her feel bad
too. But she forgot all about it when she talked to Adrian
and accepted.

The afternoon at the museum turned out far better than
she had anticipated. Norah was not particularly enthusiastic
about art exhibitions, but Adrian was a charming escort and
certainly knowledgeable. Paintings and sculptures she had
seen before, at least as reproductions, she now viewed in a
new way. He made her appreciate both the concept and the
execution, taught her what to look for. Joe had introduced
her to opera in much the same way. As they strolled through
the galleries, Norah was aware of the women looking at
Gourdine. He was handsome, she thought, though in a very

different way from Joe. She admitted she enjoyed being seen with him. Underneath though, spicing every word and each casual touch, a hand on the elbow to guide her, an accidental brush as they turned a corner, was the anticipation of the evening.

Adrian didn't ask her this time where she'd like to go; he took her to his place. And she could hardly girlishly demur. In fact, she had expected nothing else and was prepared.

The loft was large, of course. Almost bare, naturally. Wallboard partitions stood between working studio and living quarters. Adrian did not offer to show her his work. She was curious, but shy about asking to see it. She sat at the end of the sofa feeling, and knowing that she looked, nervous. The sofa was one of those sensuous modular things, down-cushioned, with space enough for at least four to cavort. Otherwise, there were only the bare necessities. The main feature of the place was a twelve-foot picture window overlooking the East River toward Brooklyn Heights, with a view of Upper New York Bay and a glimpse of the Verrezano Narrows Bridge. No decor could top it.

Adrian served the white wine Norah especially liked, then a nicely simmered pot-au-feu, salad, fresh fruit in brandy. He cleared the table, put the dishes in the dishwasher, and came back. He took Norah's hand and led her to the sofa again. He nestled close. She didn't move away. He nuzzled her neck; kissed her lightly, then more demandingly. She let him.

"Come on, Norah. Cooperate."

She tried.

His lips parted hers. His tongue entered her mouth. He pushed her back, down on the pillows, a leg entwined between hers, his hand opening her blouse and fondling her breasts. She let him. Suddenly, she pushed him away, struggled upright and walked to the other side of the room.

"I'm sorry. I can't."

Adrian was red-faced. "You're a little too old to be a tease, aren't you?"

"I'm not a tease. I just can't go through with it."

"Oh, hell." He took a deep breath, using his anger to cool off. "It's not supposed to be a sacrifice."

She nodded. "I think I'd better go." She reached for the purse she'd left on the corner of the couch. He caught her hand. She pulled free.

"Give yourself a chance, sweetheart. Give me a chance. I can make you happy."

Norah bit her lip. "I'm sure you're very talented, but I told you once before—it's not my style."

"You're holding out for marriage, is that it?"

"I'm not holding out for anything. What I believe is what I am. I can't change. I believe there is no incentive to make a relationship work without marriage. At the slightest squabble, the slightest friction, difficulty, inconvenience, it's— give up. It's give up, move out, and somebody else moves in. Until that's no fun anymore either."

"By incentive you mean children."

"Marriage is a contract. A statement of dedication to someone other than oneself."

"And to children."

"All right, yes, to children."

"Fine. So if you get pregnant, I'll marry you."

Norah stared.

"But you won't ever have a child if you don't get to work on it. You haven't many child-bearing years left. Even you, self-sufficient as you are, Sergeant Mulcahaney, can't do it alone."

He couldn't know how sensitive a spot he'd touched, Norah thought. She hadn't told him how hard she and Joe had tried to have a child or that in the happiness of their life together their inability to have a child had been the only sorrow. In fact, she hadn't confided her feelings to Adrian Gourdine at all. They hadn't really talked about any of the things that mattererd. Out of an instinct to inflict pain, he had lashed her with the one stunning insult that could really hurt.

The heat of the humiliation coursed through Norah's

whole body. How could she have allowed herself to become so vulnerable, subjected herself to his degrading?

"Of course, there's artificial insemination. Maybe that's more your style?"

She reeled. But when she recovered she was herself again. "I'm finally seeing you as you are, Adrian, and I don't like what I see."

"Oh, you like it. We know you like it."

"No, I don't. Up to now I overlooked the meanness and the selfishness, because I wanted something from you. You're right about that. From the beginning you put me down, debased what I believe in, and I took it and came back for more because subconsciously I saw you as my last chance to have a child."

He smirked and moved in close.

She looked right up into his face.

"But you aren't. You've just told me so."

Norah felt as though a load had been lifted off her. How could she have looked twice at Gourdine? Would he now make another play for Toni just to spite her? She didn't want to tell her niece about what had happened between her and the art teacher. Toni would be hurt, maybe even jealous, but she would know Norah was telling the truth. Wouldn't she? Norah hoped Gourdine wouldn't make telling Toni neces- sary, but why should she expect a favor from him? Back at work on Monday morning she put the problem aside, placed Frank Salgo's portrait on her desk, and stared at it. Sud- denly, she tore it up and threw it into the wastebasket.

Wrong, wrong, she'd been going about it all wrong! Threading her way between desks, Norah went to the cap- tain's office, knocked, and burst through.

"What we've got to do is make him come to us!" she blurted out.

It was a long shot. Putting out bait always was. And dan- gerous. Norah knew that too. She'd been a decoy before.

She had never enjoyed it. She didn't expect to enjoy it this time.

Captain Jacoby listened skeptically as she outlined the plan, but he didn't say no out of hand. He got up and opened his office window to let the cool air in. He considered her idea because it seemed the last chance to salvage the case— and his investment of man-hours in it. He was far from enthusiastic, but Norah hadn't expected enthusiasm. It was enough that he did agree at last, with the proviso that the stakeout be conducted jointly with the Nassau police. Hedging his bet.

Gary Reissig called as soon as he heard. "I wish you wouldn't do it."

"It's the only chance we've got. It may already be too late."

"I mean, why does it have to be you? This kind of duty is for somebody . . ."

"Younger?" Norah challenged.

"Yes. All right, yes. Somebody with less experience."

"You don't think the job requires experience?"

"Norah, don't quibble. You know exactly what I mean. You're too valuable to be put at risk. You've got so much ahead of you, a whole career that's just starting. There's no telling how far you can go. You have so much to offer."

"So does every rookie that comes out of the academy."

Not like you, Reissig thought, but he only sighed.

"Are you coming to the meeting?" Norah asked.

"You couldn't keep me away."

Seventeen days had passed since the heist at Mercury. Two days after that the body of the fourth victim (and Norah hoped the last), Bess Zimmer, had been discovered on the sand beside the Loop Parkway. The team met in Captain Jacoby's office. Everyone was very much aware of the anxiety expressed earlier by Norah: it might be too late as far as apprehending Frank's accomplice was concerned. He might already have skipped the country. It depended really, Norah thought, on whether Salgo had made connection with the mob again. Mob bosses were accustomed to setting up a scapegoat to take the heat while they went on comfortably with their regular business. However, it was possible that Salgo had joined with a renegade, somebody who had quit the mob and set out on his own. A man like that would take the $8 million and get out fast. Either way, she was now convinced that Frank had done the dirty work, committed the murders, and been left with the short end of the stick. Norah had noted that murderers, while they might not return to the scene of the crime as compulsively as indicated by mystery fiction, did usually stay where they were and continue with their normal lives. It was most often to protect that life-style that they killed. She believed therefore that Frank was still around and he was the one she was really after.

"Mulcahaney? Are you with us?" Jacoby growled.

"Sorry, sir. I didn't catch that."

"If you've got something more important on your mind, Sergeant, I'll excuse you. I'm sure we can find someone who will take full interest."

A task force of twelve detectives, made up from the Nassau, Queens, and Manhattan commands, was present in Jacoby's office—Gary Reissig included, of course. That would allow for a double shift to cover Norah on the job at the J. C. Marshall Company and then at home. A pair from Nassau started to snicker at the reprimand, but they didn't need sharp looks from the rest to stop them. They remembered Mulcahaney was going to be set out as the target. She had a right to be preoccupied.

"With all respect, sir, it might be a good idea for somebody else to be the decoy. The suspect may already know Sergeant Mulcahaney." Reissig had made up his mind to make the point, whether Norah liked it or not.

She glared, but he would not meet her look. Usually the media seized on any exploit of a woman police officer. In the past, she had gotten plenty of attention. Her picture had appeared in newspapers and on television: she'd had more than her share of exposure. Jacoby, however, had made it clear that he expected his people to keep a "low profile"; the "cult of personality" was not encouraged. A case successfully concluded should reflect merit on the team, the squad, and the commander. It hadn't been difficult to follow the captain's line on this one because the victims were all young and pretty enough to keep the press satisfied. Besides, Norah agreed with Jacoby's tenet, if not his way of expressing it. Here was tangible proof he was right, and she was very happy to be able to support him.

"I don't see how. My name hasn't even been mentioned in connection with the case. I'll be posing as a friend of Lila Cestone's."

"Why her? Ferdi Arenas asked

"Because she was the next-to-the-last victim."

"I don't get it."

"The story's going to be that I was a friend and I worked with Lila. Unbeknownst to her or the perpetrator, I saw her and her mystery boyfriend together a couple of times. I didn't say anything before because I was scared. But since the latest murder, Bess Zimmer's, I'm even more scared to keep quiet. So I've come forward prepared to identify him. It's his established m.o. to kill beforehand. We have to assume he'll be consistent."

"It's a long shot."

"It always is."

"The story will be released in conjunction with Mercury's offer of a reward," Jacoby told the team. He nodded for Art Potts to hand out copies of the release.

MERCURY OFFERS $100,000 REWARD FOR INFORMATION
LEADING TO ARREST AND CONVICTION OF ROBBER
Witness steps forward. Police following new lead.

"Have we found Mulcahaney an apartment?" Jacoby asked.

Reissig answered. "Yes, sir, Glendale Village; that's where Cestone lived. It gives the story added credibility and opens up two places where she might have spotted the killer with her."

"Good."

"It's a garden apartment complex. There's a new section of ten units around a small mews. There's no common lobby, but each duplex has a front and back door. Norah can occupy one, we'll take another adjoining."

"Set it up," Jacoby told him. "Brennan, you and Arenas and your team will cover Mulcahaney to and from work, and on the job."

"Right."

"She's going to be wired," Jacoby continued. "Maybe she can get him to say where he stashed the money."

"Captain!" Reissig couldn't contain himself. "He's not going to sit around and talk. This man's a brutal killer. He's going to come in with the knife in his hand and go for the jugular. Literally, Captain."

Even that hardened group paled. Norah said nothing, but her stomach turned over.

Jacoby licked his lips. "Okay. Let the FBI worry about the money. We'll collar him and they can do their thing later."

"Sir, I want to be wired. Just in case."

Jacoby was tempted. He struggled. "No," he decided. "It might induce you to take unnecessary risks."

The tension in the room eased. Brennan began to address his part of the action. "About getting Sergeant Mulcahaney back and forth from the job at J. C. Marshall—we'll have to lay out a specific route and she'll have to stick to it."

"You're not going to let her drive!" Reissig was indignant. "That's how he got each and every one of those women—in her car. That's playing right into his hands. It's giving him the opportunity he's going to be looking for."

"How else is she going to get there?" Brennan demanded.

"There's a bus."

"We can't protect her on the bus."

"He's not going to attack her on the bus."

"The car is better. Once she's in the car, she locks the door and that's it."

Reissig wouldn't give up. "That's his m.o. We've got to force him to change it."

"No," Norah interrupted. "We've got to encourage him to use it."

Norah moved into Glendale Village using her mother's maiden name, Reilly. She kept her own first name; that made the adjustment easier since people she was working with and her new neighbors quickly called her Norah. He would be observing her, she was sure. It was important that she respond naturally.

It didn't take her long to adapt to the new routine. Because she was given real work to do—sales figures to be charted, inventories taken—the time passed more quickly than in most stakeouts. It eased the strain. The bad time came when she was alone in the apartment, particularly the break for the Labor Day weekend. Disruption of the office routine necessitated increased surveillance and both Norah and the team were relieved when the holiday passed without incident. As the days added into a week and the second week began, anxiety superseded fear. Suppose he didn't take the bait? A dozen men a day were involved; they couldn't be tied up indefinitely. As the second week drew to a close, only the interest of the FBI kept the operation going. By now Salgo himself could be long gone, could at this very minute be sunning himself in Brazil or Argentina, Norah agonized. If so, then the whole exercise was futile; they wouldn't get him or his accomplice. She might as well pack up and go home and the other detectives return to their regular assignments. But that had been a possibility from the start, Norah reminded herself. So forget about it. Resolutely, Norah put it out of her mind. Sometimes to reach a solution certain assumptions had to be made.

Posit that Salgo was still around: then why wasn't he reacting? Maybe he didn't believe that she, in the person of Norah Reilly, friend of Lila Cestone, was a real threat? Alone in the borrowed apartment night after night, Norah had plenty of time to go over it.

Suppose they were baiting the wrong man?

What she now knew about young Salgo didn't even support the psychological profile of the slasher. True, as a boy he had worked for one of the major crime families and might be expected to have acquired a certain criminal sophistication. But he had been only an errand boy. On his own, what had he actually done? He'd broken into a church poorbox, then as he fled he'd knocked down an aged nun, panicked, and hacked her to death with a blunt penknife. Next, he had tried to steal from his stepfather—and, apparently, bungled that. There followed an interval of months during which nothing was known of him. He didn't surface again till the killing of Nancy Hurlock. The very next morning he stole a chalice, again from a church. Hardly a crime that required skill or guts. And why had he done it? Was he that hard up for money? Couldn't he have gotten what he needed from Nancy or from one of the other women? The timing bothered Norah.

Young Frank Salgo was handsome, certainly, but was he so devastating sexually that four women of various ages and temperaments—two of them shy and lonely, two accomplished flirts—would have been in thrall to him? Could four women differing in age, character, and circumstance have been so obsessed they readily agreed to keep the relationship secret, never even being seen with him or mentioning his name to the closest friend?

Suppose Frank Salgo wasn't the killer?

There was one person who could make a positive ID, one person who had met and talked to the slasher, turned down a date with him and lived. The receptionist at Thor Security. Mara Lynn Hoffritz.

Norah couldn't go herself, not while playing the role of Lila Cestone's friend, so Gary interviewed Mrs. Hoffritz and showed her the artist's rendering.

"No," Mara Lynn had said. "Nothing like him."

"How can you be so sure?" Reissig demanded. "You told Sergeant Mulcahaney you wouldn't know him again."

"I know this isn't him. This is a kid. If he'd come in

looking for a security job, I would have told him he was too young. I wouldn't have wasted his time or mine."

So the credibility of Norah Reilly had to be built up; her authenticity reaffirmed and with it the validity of her testimony. Different bait had to be dangled.

POLICE WITNESS FAILS TO IDENTIFY SUSPECT

"Not the man I saw," Norah Reilly claims. The only witness believed to have seen the mystery boyfriend in the company of one of his victims has failed to identify the man police suspect of having committed four brutal murders.

Under police protection for the past two weeks, Miss Reilly had been complaining of restrictions. She expressed a desire to be allowed to resume her normal routine without supervision. In order to facilitate this, she was shown a series of mug shots including one of the suspect. She failed to pick him out.

Miss Reilly will be leaving at the end of the week for a much-needed vacation.

On Tuesday morning, Norah sneaked out of the J. C. Marshall Company building by way of the underground garage for a meeting in Captain Jacoby's office with the rest of the team.

Thumb to lip, Jacoby brooded. "Now that you're ostensibly of no more use to the police, he'll look for us to remove surveillance. We will appear to do so. He'll wait a day or two to make sure we're gone and then make his move."

"What move is that, Captain?" Reissig asked.

"He's going to try to get into her car, naturally. As soon as he does, we've got him."

"That easy." Reissig sighed.

Jacoby scowled and everybody looked, and was, uncomfortable. "So what do you suggest?"

"Call if off."

"No!" Norah cut in. Chin thrust forward, she looked first to Gary but made her pitch where it counted—to Jacoby. "We can get him! What we have to do is set up an opportunity that will appeal to him. Set it up so even if surveillance should still be on, he'll feel he has a good chance of evading it and getting to me. Not at home or at the office. It should be a public place . . . a shopping center. Makes sense. I'm supposed to be leaving Saturday for a Caribbean vacation. What's more natural than going shopping? Roosevelt Field is close. He'll figure no way you could cover me in a place like that."

"And he'd be right," Reissig observed.

Norah knew as well as he the innumerable unforeseen events that could separate a decoy from her backup. "I'm not worried," she said.

"I am." Reissig insisted. "Anyhow, how's he going to follow you there? If he doesn't drive . . ."

He let it hang and nobody could come up with an answer.

Suddenly, Norah smiled and the smile grew into a triumphant grin. "So I won't drive. I won't use the car. We'll force him to work in the open. You were right at the start," she admitted to Gary. "I'll take the bus to the shopping center!"

"No, I don't like it. It's too loose." Jacoby was having grave second thoughts. The initial decoy operation had been cleared with the head of Homicide Detectives, Inspector James Felix. Jacoby would have gone to him again, made it a joint responsibility, but Felix was in Washington and so far Jacoby hadn't been able to reach him. Should he consult Chief Deland? The chief of detectives had a reputation for liking a man who made his own decisions, providing they were the right ones. If anything happened to an officer in his command, a woman, particularly this woman, who was known to the brass and well regarded . . .

"I'm calling it off."

Norah gasped. She looked to Gary; no help there—it was what he wanted. She sought Roy Brennan's eyes, then Ferdi's. What could they do? She pulled herself up ramrod straight. It was up to her to make her own case. "Captain, he's no sharpshooter coming after me from some rooftop with a telescopic sight on his rifle. His weapon is a knife. To use it, he's got to get in close, real close. That involves no more risk than any decoy on any street corner takes every night all over this city, Captain."

Despite the wide-open window and a cool September breeze, Jacoby sweated. "Okay. We'll make it Wednesday, the crowds should be a little less midweek. Okay. Brennan, you and Arenas cover Mulcahaney from the time she leaves the J. C. Marshall building to the bus stop. I want two men on the bus ahead of her . . ."

He set himself to the logistics.

At five-thirty precisely on Wednesday afternoon, Norah covered her typewriter and signaled to Roy and Ferdi down in the lobby that she was ready to leave. They signaled back the okay. So Norah Reilly left the executive and sales offices of the J. C. Marshall Company for the last time. She walked down the hall to the fifth-floor elevator and got on with a group of her fellow workers. Her backup, Ferdi Arenas, among them. As the doors closed, the speaker spewed out its usual bland Muzak selection. At the fourth floor, more passengers entered. Norah and Arenas moved to the rear, Arenas positioning himself in front of her to scrutinize each new person that got on. At the third floor bodies were jostled to make room for newcomers. Norah felt a prick, like a pin, through her silk blouse just below her left shoulder blade.

"Hello, sweetness."

It was a whisper, lascivious, at her right ear, calculated not to be overheard under the music. "Don't look around, darling, or it'll go in deep, real deep."

The next prick was more pronounced, at her right ear, but still light and quick, an indication that the knife was very sharp and the man wielding it an expert. Arenas faced front routinely watching oncoming passengers. He'd served as backup countless times; it was established procedure to watch the crowd, not the subject, and it didn't occur to him to turn around. Besides, no approach was anticipated till Norah hit the street at the earliest. Ferdi couldn't have any idea it had already been made. Yet he felt a prickly sensation at the back of his neck and a cold shiver passed through him—a premonition that something wasn't right. The car stopped on the second floor and somehow more people managed to squeeze on, pushing Norah back hard against the man with the knife. Ferdi was impelled to turn and steal one quick look. What he saw on Norah's face froze him. The suspect was there, jammed in among the passengers! What could Ferdi do? Nothing. Only turn away again and pretend he hadn't seen. It was the nightmare of Pilar all over again.

As the doors closed for the last time, the man with the knife leaned his chin over Norah's shoulder and placed his cheek close to hers.

"We're going to walk out together real close, real friendly. I want you to smile." His hot breath caressed her ear. The musk base of his cologne made her nauseous. "I said— smile." The knife flicked again, a slight but real cut. Norah could feel the blood bubble and then ooze out in a thin trickle and her lips twisted.

As the elevator stopped to unload passengers into the lobby, Ferdi Arenas was one of the first to get off. The suspect was probably holding a knife on Norah, he thought, the knife was his weapon. If that were so, Arenas could take a chance and jump him from the back. But suppose he had a gun? Gritting his teeth, Ferdi stepped to one side and let them pass.

No longer within the limited confines, the suspect put his arm around Norah across her back and rested his right hand on her shoulder close to her neck as though in a caress. In an instant, it could become a stranglehold. The knife was in his left hand, concealed between their bodies, and in a flash it could plunge into her side. Would he dare do it then and there? Would he risk his own safety? Norah believed that he would and that he would savor the display of power. She flashed a warning look at Ferdi and he fell back.

"Come on, darling," the suspect said loud and hearty for

everyone to hear. "I'm not taking no for an answer. One drink. One last, goodbye drink. You've got time for that." Low, he whispered. "Speak up, sweetheart, nice and loud and real friendly."

She obeyed. "Well, I guess I have time for one drink. Just one."

If she somehow managed to distract him and moved quickly enough, Norah thought, she might escape the full force of the knife thrust. She might, probably would, survive. Ferdi and the others deployed in the lobby would react instantly; he wouldn't get a second chance at her. The problem was the crowd. They would panic and impede the detectives. People would be in the line of fire. He'd escape. Norah set her jaw; no way she was going to let that happen.

He was keeping carefully behind her so she hadn't managed to get a look at him yet. She knew he was slightly taller than she, say six feet, thick-bodied and strong. His skin was coarse. His cheek bristly though the scent of cologne was strong enough to indicate he had shaved recently. Now was not the time to try to get a better look; now Norah was interested in trying to make eye contact with the rest of her backup. Her eyes raked the lobby. She spotted Brennan at the news stand leafing through a late edition, then Reissig at the building directory. She willed them to look her way, catch her eye and read her distress, but, of course, they were carefully avoiding that. They must see there was a man with her, a stranger. Were they fooled by his act? By hers? Did they accept him as some office bore who didn't know when he wasn't wanted, a fool who had inadvertently stumbled into the middle of the stakeout? If so, they'd be expecting her to get rid of him. And when she didn't . . . Ferdi would tell them, she thought with a sudden return of confidence.

Meantime, the man with the knife was in control. He set the pace and the direction. But Norah no longer considered resistance, not here. As he steered her through the door and out into the street, Norah was thinking ahead. Her car was parked around the corner to the right. Undoubtedly, he would head for it. The team originally assigned to cover the car had, in the new plan, been moved to the bus stop. When Roy and Gary saw her and her companion turn right toward the car, they would surely notify them to join the pursuit.

With a shove, the suspect turned Norah to the left.

He guided her around the corner and into the nearest doorway, the entrance to The Harp, a restaurant and bar and the local hangout. He was maintaining the image of a guy on the make. It would keep the detectives in doubt for a while longer.

The Harp was dark, crowded, and noisy. Immediately, he started pushing Norah through the crush around the bar toward the back as though he had spotted a table. What he spotted, what Norah knew he'd made sure of beforehand, was a rear exit. Before the detectives could even come in the front, he had her out again. And once out, he turned her again to the left.

But her car was to the right. Surely, he knew that.

For a moment, Norah was so stunned she stopped. He gave her a hard kick in the heel that sent her stumbling forward. He had not only gotten her away from her backup and eluded surveillance, but all the plans and contingencies they had so laboriously explored and attempted to anticipate were in this one turning to the left made useless. He had outsmarted them all, Norah thought. They had assumed because he didn't know how to drive he would use her car, but he could have rented a vehicle and had it delivered here. Or maybe he did know how to drive. Was she wrong about that too? Well, she'd find out soon enough.

They entered the narrow parking strip at the rear of the Marshall building adjacent to the loading dock. Everyone in shipping had long since gone. There was only one car between the dock and the railroad tracks—a four-door, dark blue, late-model Olds. He walked her around to the passenger side. The door was already unlocked; all he had to do was pull it open. He gave her a push that got her not only inside but also across the bench seat to the wheel. Then he got in himself—in the back. For a second, Norah felt as though her heart had stopped. She couldn't breathe. Searing

pain was like a vise across her chest. She should have fore-
seen this too, she thought; hadn't all the victims after Nancy
been stabbed from the back?

"Let's go." He leaned over the back of the seat and gave
her a slight push toward the ignition. The key was already
inserted.

Norah couldn't move. She was totally paralyzed.

"I said, let's go." This time he held the knife well out in
front of her where she could see the wickedly sharp blade.

A soft hiss of air escaped from her partially open mouth
releasing some tension and alleviating some of the pain. Her
heart pounded erratically. No mistake, she had the killer. Or
more accurately, he had her. Trembling, Norah reached forward and turned the key.

The engine caught, sputtered, and died. It reminded her
there were things he couldn't control, things she could do to
gain time. And time was what she needed for her backup to
catch up to her. In the original plan, before they had got
sidetracked with the shopping center, it had been assumed
the killer would accost her in her own car and a bug had
been installed, a homing device. This car was clean. So it
was up to her to buy time for them. Her handbag was slung
from her left shoulder and rested under her left arm, but she
wasn't carrying her service revolver. A gun in a handbag was
too risky when working undercover, a giveaway that could
be seized and used against the officer. Norah did have her
backup .22 in its ankle holster under her slacks.

She sneezed. "Do you have a Kleenex?"

The ordinary question took him by surprise. "No."

"Do you mind if I look in my purse?" Before he could
answer she had it in her lap, leaning over it to hide the free
hand sliding toward the holster.

He recovered instantly and snatched at the shoulder strap,
snapping her back against the seat. He yanked the bag free
and tossed it on the floor at his own feet. Almost simulta-
neously, certainly before Norah could bend any farther toward the gun, he made a cut at the base of her throat. A cut,
not a prick or a scratch.

"You want to die right here, lady?"

She turned on the ignition a second time, fed gas with the pedal, and made sure that when it caught the engine didn't stall. "Where to?" she asked and at last turned her head to look squarely at her captor. His face was broad, jowls heavy and shadowed, dark eyebrows overhung deep-set dark eyes. His nose was high-bridged, the nostrils flared. His mouth was wide and full, his lips soft and moist. He was in his late thirties and unusually handsome. Norah was not prepared for him to be so good-looking. It was not any one dominant feature, nor even the sum total, that made the impact, rather an animal magnetism. Even in this situation, she could feel it through her fear.

"Who are you?"

For answer he grabbed her hair and pulled her head back, arching her throat upward. "Move it."

"Then let go."

Seconds dragged by. It was an impasse. Finally, he released her. Each round won resulted in a subtle shift of power, Norah thought. She put the car in reverse, turned the wheel and watching over her shoulder, stepped on the accelerator. The car jumped backwards like a high-strung mare.

"Easy!" he shouted. "Easy. Now turn around and cut across the tracks."

He had planned well, Norah acknowledged, chosen a good time and place. It appeared he had succeeded very well in separating her from the men guarding her. Yet he didn't relax.

"Take a left. And get into the left lane."

That brought them to a wide avenue with a heavy but not congested flow of traffic. A large green sign indicated the left lane would feed into Sunrise Highway. While she followed instructions, Norah considered a new set of options. If she could manage to get caught at a light, she could jump out of the car and run for it. She would get away; she was sure that she would, but . . . would he? She might bring him down with her gun, but probably not: he would have too many cars to duck behind and dodge around. She had come too far to lose him like that. It was basically the same situation as in the lobby—an innocent bystander, this time a motorist, might be injured. As they entered the feed, Norah looked into the rearview mirror hoping to spot an unmarked police car. Nothing. Nobody.

The light changed. They moved into the mainstream of highway traffic picking up speed. Norah settled into a steady fifty-five, the legal limit, then stole another look at the man behind her. He was coarse, without any trace of elegance or breeding, but again she had to marvel at his good looks. And his virility was almost a crushing force. At last Norah could understand his quick and complete conquest of the victims and their almost abject willingness to do whatever he wanted—keep the relationship secret, turn over information without regard for consequences. They had been subjugated, blind to danger. She could imagine the shock and horror when they saw him for what he was and faced death at his hands.

"Who are you?" Norah asked for the second time.

"Slow down and take another left at the next light."

She had no idea where they were headed, but it was quite evident he had a specific destination in mind. Searching again in her rearview mirror, Norah found no hope or comfort. The man in the back seat was a thief and murderer, and unless she could find a weakness to exploit, he would kill her as he had the others. Since Joe's death, Norah had become a fatalist. Usually, thinking an outcome was preordained gave her strength. In this instance, it wasn't death she was afraid of, but of what the knife would do to her first.

"Do you drive?" she asked casually, talking as much to relax herself as to distract him.

Again the simple question took him unawares. "No."

She'd been right about that anyway, Norah thought. "That's unusual."

No response. His gaze was fixed on the road; Norah noticed a slight twitch at the corner of his mouth.

"Lila Cestone's boyfriend didn't drive. She told me."

"I know how to drive. I have a license. I just don't enjoy it."

"Why not?"

No answer. The silence had a determined feel to it. Norah sensed resistance. On impulse, she suddenly swerved the car.

"Watch out! My God, watch out what you're doing!" he yelled, clutching the back of the seat.

"Sorry," Norah apologized. He hung on to the seat with both hands, cringing low. "That truck was going to cut straight across us. You all right?" The irony of the remark didn't strike her till after she'd spoken.

He looked badly shaken. *Scared*, Norah thought, first with surprise, then with hope. He didn't know how to drive and he was scared. Neurotic about cars? Probably not, or he wouldn't have chosen them as the scenes for his crimes. *Speed*, maybe speed made him nervous. Just how nervous? She'd have to test him to find out. But she would also have to plan carefully. They drove in silence for the next mile and a half while Norah tried to orient herself; it would help to know where they were and if possible where they were headed. Nothing looked familiar.

"Turn right," he ordered. And slow down." He no longer hung on to the seat. The hand that held the knife was steady.

Norah did as she was told.

The turn took them from an area of modest suburban homes with small plots cluttered by flowers and tangled vegetable gardens into a vast, open, and desolate expanse of land. Piles of dirt, part sand and part gritty construction soil, were heaped as though in preparation for a mammoth project long since abandoned. Here and there clumps of dune grass rose high, heads bend under the weight of maturing seed. A line of telephone poles marched across this desert. The road was cracked, potholed, winding. Rusted car wrecks on either side. A giant, unauthorized dump, Norah thought as a 747 roared overhead, passing so low it seemed it would scrape the car roof, every rivet and every seam of its underbelly clearly visible. They were at the edge of Kennedy Airport.

"Go straight."

They crossed Rockaway Boulevard toward a cluster of gas storage tanks. To the far right, Norah glimpsed a canal or channel lined with homes. Docks extended into the water; every type of small pleasure boat was moored. These they quickly left behind. The road joined another, more frequented, dotted with gas stations and used-car lots. They passed the scene of May Guttman's death. Instinctively, Norah braked.

"Keep going."

Beach Channel Drive. She knew the area. High-rise projects fronting the ocean gave way to seaside slums—abandoned, rotted summer cottages, tarpaper shacks, a littered stretch of coarse, yellow sand. They passed under the elevated track of the Rockaway Park spur—his transportation out, Norah thought, and felt a surge of fear.

"You might as well tell me who you are. I mean, why not?" She struggled against the paralysis of her fear.

"According to you, I was Lila Cestone's boyfriend."

"I never saw you before."

"You told the police you did."

"I lied."

"You said Lila talked to you about me. Told you about me."

"No, that wasn't true either."

"Why did you lie?"

Norah searched for a plausible answer. "I wanted the reward."

That he could understand but he was still wary. "If you were after the reward, why didn't you identify the picture they showed you? Why didn't you say: yes, that's the man, and collect the money?"

"Because they showed me more than one picture. And anyway, the reward was for arrest leading to conviction. If I picked the wrong man, I wouldn't get anything."

He scowled. "But if you never saw me before, if you never

saw me with Lila, if you never saw Lila's boyfriend, then how did you know his picture wasn't in the group?" His full, sensuous lips stretched into a grim smile. "Sorry, sweetness, it won't work. One way or the other, I've got to get rid of you." He pointed to a stretch of shore about a quarter of a mile ahead. There were no buildings of any kind overlooking it. The only light came from weak, old-fashioned street lamps which barely illuminated the lonely road and certainly couldn't reach the strand or the dark, gunmetal ocean. "Pull over down there."

"I'm a police officer," Norah announced. "Sergeant Mulcahaney."

"Sure you are. Pull over."

"You don't think I'm out here alone without any backup, do you?"

"You don't think I'm so dumb I didn't watch for it?" he sneered.

The sun was low on the western horizon. Behind them to the east, it was already night. Except for the whine of the motor, there was no other sound. Even the ocean was silent.

"They saw you with me in the lobby," Norah reasoned. "They know what you look like. If anything happens to me, they'll get you."

"How will they find me?" He raised the knife so the blade glinted in the last red rays.

"You used the name Frank Salgo. They'll trace you through that. They'll check every person who ever had a connection with Salgo in his entire life. You shouldn't have used a real person's name. That was a mistake. They'll start with his mother, Mrs. Petrus, and then . . .'."

His tension was instantly transmitted. Turning from the road, Norah looked around and knew. Her heart pounded, her hands shook on the wheel. The car jerked and swerved.

"You're Petrus, aren't you? You're Homer Petrus, the second husband, the boy's stepfather."

Her hands tightened and she straightened the car. Norah didn't understand it all yet, but she knew the solution was in her grasp. "If I can figure it out, so can they. They'll get you." Gradually, Norah began to increase her speed. Apparently, he wasn't aware of it—yet.

He had a more immediate problem. "Look, uh . . . Officer . . . Sergeant. I am Homer Petrus, that's right. I am the boy's stepfather. I didn't really mean to hurt you. All I wanted was to find out how much trouble the boy was in. For his mother's sake. Magda's crazy about the kid. I threatened you to get you to tell me just how much the police have on him."

Norah's foot bore down on the accelerator with a little extra pressure.

"Frank was Lila's boyfriend, not me. He killed those girls. At first, I couldn't believe it. I didn't want to believe it. For his mother's sake. But he was his father's son and the father was no good."

"How do you know what Frank did or didn't do? Did he confess?"

"No, but . . . suddenly he had money."

"How do you know that?"

"Magda told me."

"Mrs. Petrus told me she hadn't heard from Frank since the night he attacked you and ran away."

"She wanted to protect him."

They had passed the place where Petrus had ordered her to stop, but the surroundings remained as bleak. She brought the speed up to sixty. Then sixty-five.

"Don't go so fast."

Obediently, she eased up. "You didn't know Lila Cestone?"

"Never heard of her or any of the others till I read about them in the papers. That's the truth."

Suddenly, it sprang out of Norah's subconscious—the one piece of hard evidence that would nail him. "Lila Cestone made out a check for fifteen hundred dollars to cash. It was endorsed by Frank Salgo. Handwriting experts will be able to tell who signed it, Frank or you. No matter how hard either one of you tried to disguise the handwriting, they'll know."

Homer Petrus's dark eyes glazed. The knife trembled in his hand. Then slowly, the shaking hand tightened around the haft, the eyes turned fiery red as he fixed his prey. She had gone too far, Norah realized. She had cornered him, pushed him to desperation so he had nothing to lose. Fear washed over her in hot waves as he raised the knife.

She stepped on the gas.

Hard. The pedal went down to the floor. The car jumped. So did he.

"For God's sake!"

After the initial surge, the car seemed to hesitate, to be suspended while absorbing the additional injection of fuel. Then, pulsing with power, it shot forward.

"Oh, God! Stop. Stop the car!" he screamed.

"Drop the knife. Drop it here on the seat beside me."

"Stop the car." he moaned. "Stop the car."

"Drop the knife."

With the needle wavering at seventy, Norah turned the wheel and took them into a screeching, careening U-turn. Neither one of them had seat belts on; Norah used the wheel to steady herself, but Petrus was thrown sideways so hard his head smacked the window and cracked it.

"Oh, God," he sobbed, shaking, soaked in sweat. Blood running down his cheek he reached out, opened his hand, and let the knife fall to the seat beside Norah.

She scooped it up by the tip and dropped it to the floor between her feet. He would never get it from there.

She kept at seventy all the way to the Mott Avenue station. When she pulled up, it took two cops to lift Homer Petrus off the floor where he huddled on his knees, arms clasped over his head.

He was half carried, half dragged inside and placed in a cell still incoherent. A doctor was called, then a psychiatrist. Bit by bit the grisly cause for Homer Petrus's psychotic fear was drawn from him. When he was a boy, only nine years old, he and his brother Ari had been riding with their father on the Interborough Parkway. Near Kew Gardens Interchange a car coming from the opposite direction veered over the center line and hit them head on. The top of their car sheared off, decapitating the father and the older boy beside him. Homer, crouching in the back, was spared.

Homer Petrus remained under sedation for thirty-six hours before he was judged fit to be interrogated. The FBI, the NYPD Bank and Robbery Squad, and Homicide teams from three counties took turns while the DAs of the various jurisdictions squabbled among themselves over who would prosecute. Not that the case would be all that easy to argue. In fact, even the charges weren't easy to decide. Attempted murder of a police officer was open and shut. It wasn't enough. It wasn't what the politically ambitious prosecutors were fighting over. A handwriting expert was prepared to attest that Petrus had forged his stepson's signature on Lila Cestone's check; that at least made him a prime suspect for murder. They wanted more. So did the police, from the brass down to the men and women who had actively participated in the investigation. The big break came when the lab turned up Petrus's prints on the van in which Bess Zimmer had been killed. That tied him to her murder and to the robbery, and put it all into the Nassau DA's lap. It also provided the interrogation teams with ammunition and a slight shift in direction. They concentrated on the money.

Over and over, Homer Petrus was questioned about the robbery. It was reviewed step by step: from the start when it was just an idea, an unformulated notion, through the murders, to the actual breaking and entering and the escape with $8 million in gray canvas sacks. What had he done with all those bills? Because of the bulk alone, it wouldn't be easy to hide. What had he done with it? Obviously, he had gotten rid of it before killing his accomplice; he had needed Bess to drive to the hiding place. So where in hell was the money? What had he done with it?

The FBI and the Bank Robbery detail went out to the Petrus house with a search warrant. They took the building apart, starting with Homer's Bar and Grill, then moving up to the apartment, and finally to the two tenant apartments above. They ripped the floors; they pounded on the walls, and when in doubt opened them. They dug up the basement and the backyard.

They found nothing—no cash, no safe deposit or locker key, no claim check or bill of lading.

Where in hell had the money gone? What had he done with it? Ed Dobbs, special agent in charge of the search, fumed.

Magda Petrus stood to one side and watched the destruction of her home without expression. Norah Mulcahaney watched Magda: to be stoic was one thing, not to feel, another. Norah waited till the job was done, till the place was restored, more or less. Then, when the others were leaving, she hung back.

"May I speak with you, Mrs. Petrus?"

The woman shrugged. She had been standing on her feet through the long hours while strangers had violated her home. Her dress, black cotton, cut simply but artfully, loose yet revealing every curve, was ruined by plaster dust. Plaster dust streaked her dark hair. It muted the shine of the golden chains around her neck and the bracelets on her arms. It was over all the furniture. Yet, shoulders square and back stiff, she walked into the shambles of her living room and sat on the couch, waiting for whatever Norah had to say.

Norah had encountered the families of both victims and criminals, and had always been able to pity them. Very often, those who cared for the perpetrator bore a heavier burden, for they grieved also for the violence he had wrought and had to agonize over how much of the fault might be theirs. But for this woman, for Magda Petrus, Norah couldn't feel a thing. The woman's apathy was both unnatural and out of character. She was almost arrogant in her lack of concern over what happened around her.

Norah was as dissatisfied with the day's work as the men who had just left, but not because no clue to the whereabouts of the money had turned up. As far as Norah was concerned, there was another and much more disturbing loose end.

"Where's Frank?" she asked. "Where's your son?"

Magda Petrus's face remained without expression, her eyes lackluster. She had been asked that too many times to do anything but shrug it off. "I don't know."

A sense of incompleteness continued to nag Norah. The case could not be closed till Frank Salgo was found. The relationship between the three—Magda, Homer, and the boy—stood at the core of everything that had happened.

"After Frank served his time at Spofford and was released to come home was he surprised to discover you had remarried?"

"He knew already. I wrote and told him."

"How did he take it?"

For a moment the apathy lifted. "He resented Homer. As a manchild, it was a natural reaction."

"And Homer, your new husband, how did he feel about the boy?"

"He wasn't a boy anymore. And I already told you, Homer didn't like having a full-grown man hanging around the house, living off him. He thought he ought to get out and get a job."

"How did you feel?"

That was a new question and it took time for her to formulate an answer. "I loved them both."

Norah had to remind herself that just because Magda Petrus didn't show emotion was no proof she felt none. The woman was living a nightmare and maybe to deny what she felt was the only way she could survive. "But you let your husband throw Frank out."

"Frank tried to kill him." Her voice quavered.

The first time she'd told the story, Magda had minimized the fight between the two men. "And you haven't seen Frank since that night?"

"I've said so."

And Norah didn't believe it, not now anymore than she had then. What else had Magda lied about? "You say you disapproved of Frank's working as a numbers runner and then his handling drugs, that you refused to take the money he brought home. Why didn't you make him quit his job?"

"I tried. He refused. If I had insisted, he would have run away. At least I had him home with me."

Plenty of parents with better education and higher social standing whose children used drugs or alcohol or hung out with the wrong crowd found solace with that same excuse.

"Were you working?"

"Yes. Whenever I could get work."

"Doing what?"

"You know."

"Domestic work. The money Frank brought home could have come in real handy."

Magda Petrus bit her lip and remained silent.

"It was a lot of money he brought in week after week. What did he do with it?"

No answer.

"Kids who make that kind of money have no sense of its value. They shoot baskets for a hundred dollars a throw; they buy all kinds of expensive hi-fi equipment, computer games, clothes, motorbikes. What did Frank do with it?"

Still no answer.

"It was such a lot of money, coming in so regularly. You could have lived more than comfortably on it, you could have lived lavishly. You could even have put something aside so that when Frank went to jail, you wouldn't have had to go back to work, not for a long time."

"I'd been working."

"You said intermittently. As a domestic."

"I'm not ashamed." The flush suffusing her face contradicted her.

"Who did you work for? Give me a name."

"It's none of your business."

"I think it is. Oh, yes, Mrs. Petrus, I think it is." Norah's eyes flashed; she raised her chin. No more floundering; she knew now exactly where she was headed. "You didn't like cleaning other women's houses." Any more than you like cleaning your own, she added mentally.

Now she had a different slant on Magda—her dirty house, her expensive clothes, her scent, her fake jewelry.

She no longer saw Magda as a woman torn between her roles of mother and wife, but as self-indulgent, a woman who would stop at nothing to get what she wanted. "You didn't slap Frank and throw the money back at him. You took it. You used it. Lived on it. And when he went to jail, you found another man to support you. Homer Petrus. Only what Homer could offer from the bar and grill downstairs wasn't enough. You were used to better things. When Frank got out you expected he would provide as he had before. Only when he tried to go back to his old job, they didn't want him. He had grown up." Norah paused for a moment. "You were bitterly disappointed. You made no secret of how you felt—and you let both your men know it."

The flush faded, Magda Petrus's face was stone. "I'm very tired, Sergeant Mulcahaney. Would you please get to the point, if there is one."

"Who got the idea for the Mercury Courier Service robbery? Who knew enough about the company to even fantasize about such a thing?"

She shrugged. "Ask Homer."

"I'm asking you."

"I don't know anything about it."

"Was it Frank's idea? Did he meet Nancy Hurlock at the lunch counter near the bank by accident, start seeing her because he really did like her? Did he tell you about Nancy? Confide in you? Did he mention her father was an executive of Mercury and she had worked for him?"

It all made sense, Norah thought: the pressure on the boy when he got out of detention to bring money home; his desire to give his mother what she demanded; his unhealthy desire to please her. Frank Salgo had robbed the poorbox of Our Lady of Perpetual Help and when Sister Therese surprised him as he was running away, he had been forced to kill her. It had been done clumsily, perhaps even reluctantly, Norah thought, visualizing the scene on the church steps. Why did he kill Nancy Hurlock? She thought of the picnic in the park never eaten, the cloth spread out on the grass, then refolded and returned to the hamper.

"Frank left home, but he couldn't stay away from you, not for long. He loved you. So he kept in touch. He visited you. He told you about Nancy. He liked her. He sensed his feeling for you was wrong, so he tried to love Nancy, but he couldn't. He betrayed her to you."

A glint of satisfaction flashed in Magda's eyes and was gone, but not before Norah caught it.

"You planned the robbery based on the information Frank got from Nancy and brought to you."

The woman remained stolidly silent and expressionless, her well-manicured hands kneaded the fabric of her dress.

"You were the brains behind everything," Norah continued. It didn't hurt to leaven accusation with flattery. "You used your son *and* your husband. You sent Frank to get all the information he could out of Nancy Hurlock. Was it that she didn't know enough? Or that she got suspicious at the way Frank questioned her? Maybe both? Anyway, you decided she had to be silenced. You set it up for Frank to do, but you didn't trust him so you sent Homer around to check on him. Lucky for you that you did, because Frank hadn't even shown up for the date. Nancy was sitting in the park with her picnic basket waiting with the meal laid out. It got dark. She gave up and packed everything away again. Then she thought she saw Frank coming toward her. She ran up the hill, hamper in hand, relieved, eager. She raised her lips. It wasn't Frank. She dropped the hamper. Before she could turn away, Homer drew the knife across her throat.

"Unfortunately, Nancy's death left you with gaps in the information you needed. So you went after it. The pattern had worked once; you assumed it would work again. *You* chose the most likely informant. When you had what you needed you had her eliminated, just like Nancy, before she could start to wonder why her new boyfriend was asking such odd questions. And, of course, you couldn't take a chance on Frank anymore. He had proved unreliable. It was Homer all the way from then on. He used Frank's name. It seemed a smart precaution."

"I'm very tired," Magda Petrus said and got up. "I'm going to my room to rest."

Norah stepped in front of her. "What about the chalice?"

"What chalice?" She passed a hand wearily across her eyes. "Oh, yes, the one from the church. I don't know anything about that either, Sergeant. Now, please . . ."

House-proud Lila Cestone had only possessed the beautiful vessel for a few days before her death but she had polished it until it shone. Whatever fingerprints had been on it were gone. Since Norah agreed with Father Boylan that it was unlikely a stranger had wandered into the church and committed the theft, she could absolve Petrus of this one offense at least. "Frank stole the chalice for you, didn't he." It was statement rather than question. Norah knew the answer; just about all of it at last.

"Frank liked Nancy and wanted to love her. He tried. But he couldn't because he loved you. Caring for her meant he was being untrue to you. Yet you were his mother. When you told him to get rid of her, he was willing. He felt that he had to punish Nancy for having come between the two of you, and of course, he wanted to please you. He had used his knife to kill before and he thought it would be easy to do it again. But at the last minute he couldn't."

Norah paused for a moment reviewing the chronology of Frank Salgo's impotence and confusion, fleshing out the details in her mind.

"I think he did actually go to the park and to the meeting place. I think he waited, unobserved, trying to screw up his courage. It got dark. Nancy started to pack up. She'd be going. He couldn't put it off any longer. It was now or never. Then Homer appeared. Your husband saw that the girl was leaving and he took matters into his own hands.

"Frank watched helplessly as his stepfather committed the brutal murder, watched him do what he hadn't the guts for, and knew you would reward Homer. When it was over, Frank turned and ran. He couldn't go back to you; you'd be furious. He couldn't face you. Probably, he wandered all night; Frank was no stranger to the streets. In the morning, he found himself in the old neighborhood. He remembered the church and knew it was opened early. There would be money there, he thought, and if he brought you money, you might forgive him."

Magda's face remained blank, yet Norah was sure that she was making an impact.

"There was no money. The poorbox was bolted down; he couldn't pry it loose. Then Frank saw the chalice. It gleamed on the altar. All he had to do was take it. It was so easy— take it, walk out, sell it, and then give you the money. He was elated. But in his confusion and in his fear of being caught, Frank couldn't even do that. He tried for nearly two weeks to get rid of it. In the end, he made you a direct gift."

As far as Norah was concerned, the woman's very lack of reaction was admission of guilt. "It came at a good time," she went on. "By then Homer had killed May Guttman and was getting the last information you needed from Lila Cestone. You'd found a driver, Bess Zimmer, but to make sure of her you needed money to supply her habit. So you took the chalice your son had stolen to buy your love and handed it over to your husband, who was killing for you. Homer was to dispose of it. He did it in what he thought was a smart and safe way." And that had been mistake number two, Norah thought, and a fleeting frown from Magda indicated she was well aware of it. Norah paused and took a breath. "Where's Frank?" she asked.

"I don't know."

Was it possible Frank Salgo had the money? Norah wondered. "You do know. You must know. The three of you were in this together from the beginning . . ." Norah stopped as the full extent of Magda Petrus's guilt became apparent. In that first interview, playing the part of the anxious mother, Magda had revealed her son's criminal record to Norah, a police officer. While ostensibly pleading for compassion, she had cunningly depicted Frank Salgo as exactly the type capable of committing the crimes Norah was investigating. With full intent she had focused attention on Frank and away from her husband. And so the whole, ugly, cold-blooded scheme was now revealed. It was as shocking as any crime Norah had ever dealt with.

"The three of you were in it together *only* at the beginning," she stated. "Frank didn't commit the first murder and he didn't commit any of the others." A terrible premonition of how it had all ended turned Norah to ice.

"Where's Frank?" she demanded. "What's happened to him?"

Magda Petrus tried to pass.

Norah wouldn't let her. "In God's name, he was your son!"

"No." At last the mask broke, but it revealed neither sorrow nor pain, nor even fear. It was distorted by a resentment that was close to hate. "He was my first husband's son, Stefan's. Stefan walked out on me. Stuck me with another woman's kid. They owed me. Both of them."

"Did Frank know he wasn't your son?"

Magda Petrus raised her head and looked straight into Norah's eyes. "No."

"Where is he?" Norah demanded.

She didn't flinch. "I don't know what Homer did with him." She stepped around Norah and walked out.

Norah didn't try to stop her.

"We can't arrest her. What can we charge her on?"

Manny Jacoby asked aloud the questions Norah had put to herself over and over again. "Accessory before the fact? After the fact? Conspiracy to commit murder? Grand theft? She's guilty of every one and we can't touch her."

"And she knows it."

"According to what I hear from the Nassau DA's office, they're not even going to bring Magda into it. It would serve no useful purpose and would only muddy the case against Homer."

Norah hadn't expected anything else, but she sighed nevertheless.

"I'm sorry, Norah."

She looked up in surprise. Their eyes met. Jacoby smiled. "They'll be watching her though. Constantly. Thanks to you."

Norah smiled back.

Ostensibly, Gary Reissig was in town to wrap up any loose ends on the case. He invited Norah to dinner but she couldn't make it. She was finally meeting Jake and Lena to close the door once and for all on Adrian Gourdine. It couldn't be postponed any longer. So Gary bought her lunch in the park. They ate hamburgers seated at an umbrella-topped table beside the lake. The air was crisp, the September sun warm, the water so still it offered a picture reflection of trees and sky. There wouldn't be many more days like this, Gary thought. Maybe this would be the last one he would share with Norah.

"We could interrogate Magda once more," he suggested. "We'd have to get permission from the defense, of course, but there's a good chance . . ."

"It wouldn't be any use. She's a survivor. She knows all she has to do is keep her mouth shut." Contentedly, Norah bit into her hamburger and leaning back, raised her face to the sun as she chewed.

"Well, maybe Homer will decide to talk. He can certainly implicate her. If he does . . ." Reissig was trying to keep it going.

Norah shook her head, swallowed. "Why should he? He's committed four indictable homicides—five, counting Frank Salgo and assuming his body is ever found. There isn't much room for plea bargaining," she remarked with irony. "And how much credibility can Homer Petrus inspire?"

"So she walks," Gary muttered, glum on both counts. He was surprised Norah took it so easily. "She gets off scot-free."

Norah stopped chewing. Her dark blue eyes gleamed. "Until she goes after the money. You've forgotten the money, Gary. She's got to know where it is, right?"

"Sure."

"When Bess Zimmer's body was found, the van was empty and headed back toward Long Beach. So it makes sense the money was already stashed, probably in sealed moisture-proof barrels, plastic ones to foil metal detectors, and buried somewhere on the empty stretch of shore from there to Montauk. I don't think it's in a locker at Jones Beach."

Reissig frowned. He was more puzzled than ever by Norah's insouciance.

"Anyhow, Magda Petrus knows where it is. And she knows she's being watched. The FBI, the Robbery Squad, the insurance company—they're not giving up. Already there's a five-hundred-thousand-dollar reward posted for information leading to recovery. Besides the pros there'll be a horde of amateurs looking to collect. She won't be able to touch a single dollar bill because as soon as she goes for it, we'll get her." Norah's eyes became somber. "We'll get her for every drop of blood leached out of those women's bodies. We'll get her for every moment of terror they suffered before expiring. She'll have to wait and while she's waiting she'll have to go back to work. She'll be scrubbing floors when she could be living in luxury, knowing she's got $8 million stashed away and can't spend a dime. It'll eat at her insides like acid. Finally, she won't be able to stand it anymore. She'll convince herself we've gotten tired of watching, or sloppy, or maybe even that we've forgotten. Then she'll make her move."

"That could take years."

Norah's face tightened. "The longer the better."

"Where's Toni?"

Norah had left Gary at the precinct, still going through reports, and arrived early at the DeVecchis' anxious to get an unpleasant discussion over. She was sitting in her usual place at the right end of the sofa sipping white wine.

Lena, on her way back to the kitchen to baste the roast,

threw the answer over her shoulder. "She's out on a date."

"No!"

Lena stopped and turned. "Why not? What's wrong?"

"Did she know I was coming? You shouldn't have let her go."

"Why not? What are you talking about? He's a perfectly nice, decent . . ."

"No, no, he's not. You don't know anything about him. Oh, Lord, I let it go too long. I shouldn't have let it go." Norah sighed. "Okay. To start with, he's too old for her."

Lena, at the kitchen door, and Jake, working at his desk, exchanged glances. Her finely arched brows were raised. He merely shrugged.

"Too old?" they both said.

"He's got to be pushing forty. And he's using Toni." Norah hesitated. "I don't want this to get back to her. I don't want her feelings hurt. But I think he's using Toni to get to me."

Jake put his pen down. His pleasant, homely face was perplexed. "Who is?"

"What do you mean who? Adrian Gourdine, of course. Her art teacher."

"Oh," Lena grinned and breathed a sigh of relief. "Toni's not taking art lessons anymore. She's into skating."

"What?"

"Sure. She's met a boy. Pete Simms. Sixteen, short hair, nice manners. He's a figure skater, very good. He won the New York state regionals last year. So now Toni's taken up skating and they're into ice-dancing. They practice together four hours every day. They're talking about making the Olympics. I think they can do it."

Norah gasped. "You knew."

"Sure we did. She's our only child. And we watch her very carefully," Jake replied.

Lena went over and kissed Norah's cheek. "It was only a schoolgirl crush." She headed for the kitchen.

Jake got up and went to Norah and kissed her too. "Thanks for caring."

Norah flushed. "There's no fool like a lonely fool." She put her wine aside and got up. "Listen," she called loudly enough so Lena would hear her. "Do you mind if I don't stay for dinner? I have a friend in town. Maybe it's not too late to catch him."